ELECTROMAGNETISM
AND ELECTROSTATICS
USING SI UNITS

Electromagnetism and Electrostatics using SI Units

W. F. Archenhold, B.Sc., F.Inst.P.

Lecturer in the Education Department,
The University of Leeds, formerly
Head of the Physics Department,
Huddersfield New College

Oliver & Boyd

Oliver & Boyd
Croythorn House
23 Ravelston Terrace
Edinburgh EH4 3TJ

A Division of Longman Group Limited

First published 1969
Second edition 1971
Reprinted 1973

ISBN 0 05 002470 1

Set in Monotype 10/12 pt Times and Univers
and printed in Great Britain by
Lowe & Brydone (Printers) Ltd.
Thetford, Norfolk

Contents

Note to Second Edition

In this edition I have corrected some minor errors and I am most grateful to colleagues who pointed these out to me. I have also modified the two sections involving the Avogadro constant, and made it clearer that Ohm's law is a special case of the general relation $V = I \times R$.

Now that SI is more firmly established, I have replaced the *weber per metre squared* by the unit name *tesla*, and I have adopted the convention that the symbol for a physical quantity represents the magnitude times the unit. I have therefore changed phrases such as 'the current I ampere which . . .' to 'the current I which . . .'.

I have also incorporated recommendations made in the 1969 A.S.E. Report on 'SI Units, Signs, Symbols and Abbreviations'. An important consequence is that the quantities *magnetic moment* and *intensity of magnetisation* are now referred to as *electromagnetic moment* and *magnetic polarisation* respectively.

W. F. A.

Leeds
April 1971

Preface

This book presents a course of study in electromagnetism, magnetism and electrostatics using the internationally accepted SI units, known until 1960 as the rationalised m.k.s.a. system of units. It is aimed at sixth-form standard or equivalent, but it should also serve the needs of students in further education who wish to become acquainted with the use of SI units in their electrical studies.

The general approach is by the two-vector (Sommerfeld) method, which is in line with the recommendations in 'The 1966 Report on the Teaching of Electricity', published by John Murray for The Association for Science Education. Magnetic fields are described in terms of the magnetic flux density B, without the introduction of H, the magnetic field strength (or magnetising force). Electric fields are described in terms of electric field strength E without the introduction of electric displacement density D. From the point of view of simplicity, the two-vector method clearly has the advantage over the four-vector (Kennelly) method, advocated in 'The Teaching of Electricity—with special reference to the use of m.k.s. units' (published for the Science Masters' Association by John Murray in 1954), in that it avoids the B–H and E–D dualisms. Moreover, the 'parallel field' approach of the 1954 Report has not found favour among the great majority of teachers.

The development of electrostatics in this book is based on the more traditional 'radial field' approach. Electric field strength E is defined in terms of the force experienced by unit charge in an electric field and Coulomb's law of force is the starting point in the quantitative work on electrostatics.

Magnetic flux density B is defined with reference to the force on a current-carrying conductor in a magnetic field, and the Biot-Savart equation is approached by experimental work on circular coils.

The essential unity of electricity and magnetism is emphasised throughout. Each major step forward in the logical development of the subject is based on a combination of theory and experiment.

Worked numerical examples in the text and questions asked at the end of each chapter total over 100. The aim of the questions is to test understanding of basic principles, both qualitative and quantitative, and to give practice in answering questions set in recent years by the Examining Bodies.

Acknowledgements

I wish to express my thanks to all those colleagues in the profession who have helped in any way to formulate the ideas contained in this book. I am grateful to my laboratory technician, Mr P. Wallis, for making much of the apparatus from constructional notes to be found in the 1954 and 1966 Reports. (Suitable apparatus is also available from some of the manufacturers.) Sincere thanks are due to my wife, who typed the manuscript, and to my colleagues in the Physics Department of Huddersfield New College, who have helped to test this material over a period of four years on some two hundred sixth-formers.

I am very grateful to the various Examining Bodies for granting permission to reprint questions set recently at the Advanced and Special levels of the General Certificate of Education, at the Higher Grade of the Scottish Certificate of Education, and in the Bachelor of Education papers of the Universities of Aberdeen and Edinburgh.

The key to the acknowledgements made after each question set by an Examining Body is as follows:

(A.E.B.)	Associated Examining Board
(C.)	University of Cambridge Local Examinations Syndicate
(J.M.B.)	Joint Matriculation Board
(L.)	University of London School Examinations Council
(O. & C.)	Oxford and Cambridge Schools Examination Board
(S.)	Southern Universities' Joint Board
(W.)	Welsh Joint Education Committee
(S.C.E.)	Scottish Certificate of Education
(B.Ed. Aberdeen)	University of Aberdeen, Bachelor of Education examination
(B.Ed. Edinburgh)	University of Edinburgh, Bachelor of Education examination

W. F. ARCHENHOLD

Huddersfield,
September 1968

Introduction to SI Units

The abbreviation SI (which is the same in all languages), stands for *'Système International d'Unités*. This name was internationally adopted in 1960 for the rationalised and coherent system of units based on the four m.k.s.a. units (metre, kilogramme, second and ampere), and on the kelvin, the unit of temperature, and the candela, the unit of luminous intensity. The mole, the seventh basic SI unit, is defined as the amount of substance of a system which contains as many elementary units as there are carbon atoms in 0.012 kg of carbon –12.

The following are the definitions of the three basic mechanical units: The *metre* is defined equal to 1 650 763·73 wavelengths, *in vacuo*, of a specified line in the emission spectrum of krypton. The metre used to be defined as the distance between two marks on a bar of platinum, but the accuracy required of modern standards made this definition unsuitable. The *kilogramme* is the mass of a lump of platinum kept under controlled conditions at Sèvres in Paris. The *second* is defined as the interval occupied by 9 192 631 770 cycles of the radiation corresponding to a specified transition of the caesium–133 atom when unperturbed by exterior fields.

The unit of force, the newton, is defined as the force which gives a mass of 1 kilogramme an acceleration of 1 metre second^{-2}, and the unit of work (energy), the joule, is the work done when a force of 1 newton moves its point of application through 1 metre in the direction of the force. These units are not only the theoretical units (like the dyne and erg), but they also serve as the practical units. The fact that SI units are coherent and serve as theoretical and practical units is a great advantage. Thus in electricity, *one* set of units replaces *three*, two theoretical—the c.g.s. electromagnetic (e.m.u.) and the c.g.s. electrostatic (e.s.u.) systems—and the practical system of units, which are decimal multiples of the theoretical units, together with all the necessary conversion factors from one system to the other.

SI units are rationalised, which also helps in a study of electro-magnetism and electrostatics. In unrationalised formulae, the factor π appears in quite illogical places, because 4π lines of flux are considered to radiate from a mythical isolated pole. Rationalisation does not reduce the number of π's in rationalised formulae, but the π's do appear where one would expect them, i.e. 4π in formulae with spherical symmetry, 2π in formulae with cylindrical symmetry, and no π's in formulae with plane symmetry.

The following tables introduce the names of the SI units required in a study of electricity, and the unit symbols. The conversion factors will help the student using SI units for the first time.

SI Units

Basic SI units used in this book

Physical quantity	Symbol	SI unit	Unit symbol
length	l	metre	m
mass	m	kilogramme	kg
time	t	second	s
electric current	I	ampere	A
temperature	θ	kelvin	K
amount of substance	n	mole	mol

Some derived SI units with complex names

Physical quantity	Symbol	SI unit	Unit symbol
area	A	square metre	m^2
volume	V	cubic metre	m^3
density	ρ	kilogramme per cubic metre	$kg\ m^{-3}$
velocity	v	metre per second	$m\ s^{-1}$
angular velocity	ω	radian per second	$rad\ s^{-1}$
acceleration	a	metre per second squared	$m\ s^{-2}$
electric field strength	E	volt per metre	$V\ m^{-1}$
electromagnetic moment	m	ampere metre squared	$A\ m^2$

Some derived SI units having special names

Physical quantity	Symbol	SI unit	Unit symbol
force	F	newton	N $= \text{kg m s}^{-2}$
work, energy	W	joule	J $= \text{N m}$
power	P	watt	W $= \text{J s}^{-1}$
electric charge	Q	coulomb	C $= \text{A s}$
electric potential electromotive force	V E }	volt	V $= \text{W A}^{-1}$
electric capacitance	C	farad	F $= \text{A s V}^{-1}$
electric resistance	R	ohm	Ω $= \text{V A}^{-1}$
frequency	f, v	hertz	Hz $= \text{s}^{-1}$
magnetic flux	ϕ	weber	Wb $= \text{V s}$
magnetic flux density	B	tesla	T $= \text{Wb m}^{-2}$
inductance	L	henry	H $= \text{V s A}^{-1}$

Conversion Factors from c.g.s. to SI Units

Physical quantity	c.g.s. unit	= factor × SI unit
length	1 cm	$= 10^{-2}$ m
mass	1 g	$= 10^{-3}$ kg
force	1 dyn	$= 10^{-5}$ N
work, energy	1 erg	$= 10^{-7}$ J
density	1 g cm^{-3}	$= 10^{3}$ kg m^{-3}
electric current	1 e.m.u.	$= 10$ A
electric charge	1 e.s.u.	$= \dfrac{10^{-9}}{3}$ C
electric potential	1 e.m.u.	$= 10^{-8}$ V
	1 e.s.u.	$= 3 \times 10^{2}$ V
electric field strength	1 e.s.u.	$= 3 \times 10^{4}$ V m^{-1}
electric capacitance	1 e.s.u.	$= \dfrac{10^{-9}}{9}$ F
electric resistance	1 e.m.u.	$= 10^{-9}$ Ω
magnetic flux	1 maxwell	$= 10^{-8}$ Wb
magnetic flux density	1 gauss (1 oersted in air)	$= 10^{-4}$ T
magnetic field strength	1 oersted	$= \dfrac{10^{3}}{4\pi}$ A m^{-1}
inductance	1 e.m.u.	$= 10^{-9}$ H

Examples Illustrating the Conversion from c.g.s. to SI Units

(values are given correct to 2 decimal places)

Velocity of light in vacuo	In c.g.s.
$c = 3 \cdot 00 \times 10^{10}$ cm s^{-1} $= 3 \cdot 00 \times 10^{10} \times \dfrac{(10^{-2} \text{ m})}{\text{s}}$ $= 3 \cdot 00 \times 10^{8}$ m s^{-1}	Molecular wt. of copper $= 64$ In SI (for copper) Relative molecular mass $= 64$ Molar mass $= 0 \cdot 064$ kg mol^{-1}
Electronic charge $e = -4 \cdot 80 \times 10^{-10}$ e.s.u. of charge $= -4 \cdot 80 \times 10^{-10} \times \left(\dfrac{10^{-9}}{3} \text{ C} \right)$ $= -1 \cdot 60 \times 10^{-19}$ C	Horizontal component of earth's magnetic flux density $B_x = 0 \cdot 18$ gauss (oersted in air) $= 0 \cdot 18 \times (10^{-4}$ T$)$ $= 1 \cdot 8 \ \times 10^{-5}$ T

Note: 1 calorie $= 4 \cdot 1868$ J   (exactly)
permeability of free space μ_0 $= 4\pi \times 10^{-7}$ H m^{-1} (exactly)
permittivity of free space ε_0 $= 8 \cdot 85 \times 10^{-12}$ F m^{-1} (exptl. result)

Prefixes used to indicate decimal multiples and sub-multiples

Factor by which the unit is multiplied	*Prefix*	*Symbol*	*Example*	
10^{6}	mega	M	MΩ	megohm
10^{3}	kilo	k	kHz	kilohertz
10^{-2}	centi	c	cm	centimetre
10^{-3}	milli	m	mH	millihenry
10^{-6}	micro	μ	μA	microampere
10^{-12}	pico	p	pF	picofarad

Chapter 1

The Electric Current

Atomic Structure

Any study of electricity and magnetism is fundamentally concerned with a study of the behaviour of electric charges. What are the main properties of 'this something' which is called electric charge? A simple experiment provides important evidence.

Two strips of polythene are rubbed in turn with a dry wool duster and one of the strips is fixed in a stirrup which is suspended

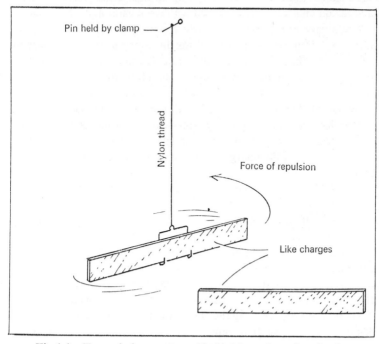

Fig 1.1   *Two polythene strips rubbed with wool repel each other*

freely from a retort stand by nylon thread (see fig. 1.1). When the second rubbed polythene strip approaches the suspended strip, there is a force of repulsion. A similar experiment, using two strips of cellulose acetate rubbed with a wool duster, gives the same result. However, when one of the charged polythene strips is brought near a charged acetate strip, there is an attractive force between the strips. Hence it is concluded that there are two types of electric charge, and that

Like charges repel, unlike charges attract.

No third type of charge can be found which will repel, say, both of two charges which attract one another. Hence two, and only two, types of electric charge exist and these are called positive and negative.

It now becomes necessary to specify which strip has the negative charge, and which strip the positive charge. Quite arbitrarily from a physical standpoint, and guided only by the history of the subject, it is decided that a polythene strip rubbed with wool gains a negative charge and an acetate strip rubbed with wool gains a positive charge.

A property of electric charge which has an important bearing on atomic structure is the experimental discovery in the early part of this century that electric charge is not 'continuous', but is in fact always made up of an integral number of a tiny quantum of a charge e, which has a magnitude of 1.6×10^{-19} coulomb. This basic building block of electric charge is so small that the particulate nature of charge does not show up in any large-scale experiments, e.g. when a charge appears on a dry plastic strip rubbed on a sleeve. However, the magnitude of the charge Q on the plastic strip can be expressed by the equation

$$Q = Ne \qquad (1.1)$$

where N is the number of basic charges and e is either the positive or negative quantum of charge.

Just as charge is found to be *quantised*, so other experimental evidence and theoretical interpretation has led to the inescapable conclusion that matter, and indeed electromagnetic radiation, are also quantised and not continuous. This evidence accumulated in the period of time covering the end of the nineteenth century and the beginning of the twentieth century, and led to the formulation of the laws of quantum physics, which have been successful in explaining many phenomena on the atomic scale where the laws of classical physics are insufficient.

Matter-in-bulk is found to be composed of atoms which are themselves made up of three elementary particles: the electron, the proton and the neutron. The masses and charges of these particles relative to the electron are shown in Table 1.1.

Table 1.1.   The mass and charge of the three elementary particles making up atoms.

Particle	Symbol	Mass	Charge
electron	e	m_e	$-e$
proton	p	$1836m_e$	$+e$
neutron	n	$1839m_e$	zero

Experiments such as the Perrin Experiment in which electrons charge an electroscope, show that the charge carried by electrons is similar to the charge on a polythene strip rubbed with wool, and hence a *negative* charge is always associated with the electron.

Investigations in the fields of radioactivity, atomic physics and nuclear physics have provided sufficient evidence for scientists to conclude that each atom of matter has a closely packed nucleus which is made up of protons and neutrons and which contains nearly all the mass of the atom. The nucleus of an atom is surrounded by a cloud of electrons at distances which are large relative to the diameter of the nucleus. The electrons may be considered to be orbiting the nucleus at great frequencies.

In an undisturbed atom, the number of electrons are equal to the number of protons and the atom is electrically neutral: the material-in-bulk made up of these atoms or groups of atoms is electrically neutral. However, not all atoms hold their outer electrons equally tightly, and this fact alone determines many of the electrical properties of a material.

Electric Charges at Rest

Why does a polythene strip rubbed with wool become charged with negative electric charges? Does a *conservation law* apply to electric charge as it does to mass-energy? If so, does the wool duster gain a positive electric charge equal to the negative charge gained by the polythene strip?

A wool duster and polythene strip are discharged by holding them near a flame for a few seconds. The wool duster is folded into a

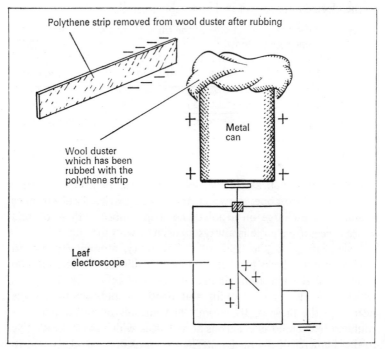

Fig 1.2 *After rubbing together, the negative charge on the polythene strip equals the positive charge on the wool duster*

metal can standing on the cap of a leaf electroscope—shown in fig 1.2. The strip is rubbed against the wool for some time and then the polythene strip is removed. The leaf rises indicating that a charge has been produced on the wool. If the strip is now replaced, the leaf falls again to its zero position, showing that the charges produced are equal in magnitude and opposite in sign. This latter conclusion may be confirmed by once more removing the polythene strip and bringing up to the can a positively charged acetate strip. This causes the leaf to rise further indicating that the charges on the leaf, can, and duster are the same as on the acetate strip, i.e. positive.

In terms of the ideas of simple atomic structure, the above experiment on the conservation of charge is explained by saying that as a result of friction between the wool and polythene, a transfer of electrons takes place from the wool to the polythene. A transfer of N electrons to the polythene creates a deficiency of N electrons in the wool, and hence a positive charge is detected on the wool.

Polythene, acetate, glass and ebonite are examples of materials which can be charged by friction. Once charged, the material retains its excess negative or positive charge for a considerable period of time. Such materials are classed as *insulators*; they do not allow electric charge to pass through them. If a metal, such as brass, is rubbed in one part, it is found to be charged all over. Brass is an example of a *conductor*, which allows electric charge to move through the material. Thus static electric charge can be obtained on an insulator, or on a conductor which must be insulated from other conductors such as the human body or the earth.

A study of the properties of static charges and their effects comes under the heading of Electrostatics to be discussed in chapters 5 and 6.

Electric Charges in Motion

Is there a connection between static electricity obtained by friction, and current electricity?

A machine which produces electric charge by friction and causes the charge to build up on an insulated domed conductor is the Van-de-Graaff generator. To test the sign of this charge, a negatively charged leaf electroscope is moved towards the charged dome. If the leaf rises further, the dome must also be negatively charged— the dome has an excess of free electrons. The capacity of the dome to store large quantities of electric charge is impressively demonstrated when a discharge occurs between the dome and an earthed metal sphere. A gentler discharge is achieved by making the continuously arriving electrons on the dome flow through a 1 megohm resistor to earth. If a sensitive centre-reading galvanometer, e.g. a 'Scalamp', is inserted in the circuit, a reasonably steady deflection is obtained on the galvanometer (see fig 1.3). Suppose the deflection is to the right of the zero position.

The Van-de-Graaff generator is now replaced by a 2 V accumulator (see fig 1.4). When the circuit is made, a steady deflection is obtained on the galvanometer, showing that there is a definite connection between electric charges produced by a friction process and then set into motion, and an electric current.

There is one further step to be taken in this experiment. Suppose that with the accumulator in position, the deflection on the galvano-meter is again to the right of zero, then this observation at once identifies the negative terminal of the accumulator. The lead which originally made contact with the negatively charged dome of the Van-de-Graaff generator is now seen to be connected to the black terminal of the accumulator. Hence the black terminal is negative and the red terminal is positive in terms of the original definition that a polythene strip rubbed with wool has a negative charge. The actual movement of the negative charge (electrons) is in a direction from the negative terminal of an electrical supply, through the ex-ternal circuit, and then to the positive terminal. This direction of *electron flow* is opposite to the direction of flow of positive charge, which is called the *conventional current direction*.

The Ampere and Coulomb

An electric current can be detected by its heating, chemical and magnetic effects. Prior to 1960, the unit of electric current, i.e. the ampere, was defined in terms of its chemical effect. Since 1960, however, the internationally accepted definition of the unit of electric current has been based on the magnetic effect because it is necessary to maintain this electrical standard to a very high degree of accuracy, and this can be achieved by the use of standard current balances based on the magnetic effect of an electric current. The decision to use the mutual force between current-carrying conductors to define the unit of current is then a practical one, and it should be noted that the ampere, defined as follows, has been chosen as the basic unit of electricity. *Definition of the ampere*: 'The Ampere is the strength of that constant current which, flowing through two parallel, straight, infinitely long conductors of negligible circular cross-section placed *in vacuo* at a distance of 1 metre apart, produces between these two conductors a force of 2×10^{-7} newton per metre of their length.'

The choice of the particular value for the force per unit length makes the ampere, as defined above, similar to the ampere as pre-viously defined by the chemical effect.

A simple qualitative experiment which demonstrates the force between adjacent current-carrying conductors is illustrated in fig 1.5.

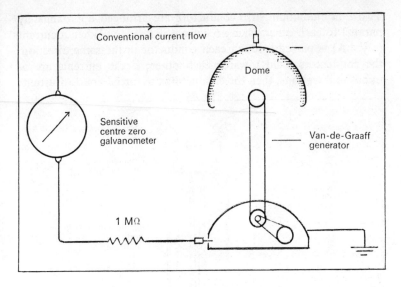

Fig 1.3 *Static electricity discharging slowly through a current-measuring light beam galvanometer*

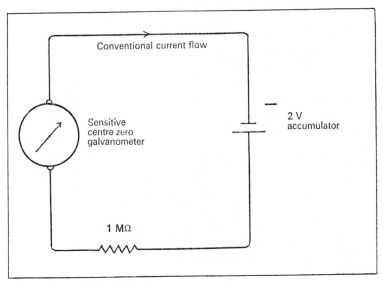

Fig 1.4 *Cell electricity passing through the same galvanometer as in fig 1.3*

Two thin aluminium strip conductors are arranged approximately parallel to each other when no current is flowing. When a current (say 4 A) is passed through each conductor in the same direction, the conductors bend towards each other; if the currents are in opposite directions, then the conductors are forced apart. Currents

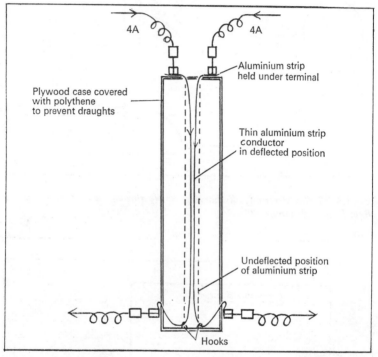

4A   4A

Aluminium strip
held under terminal

Plywood case covered
with polythene
to prevent draughts

Thin aluminium strip
conductor
in deflected position

Undeflected position
of aluminium strip

Hooks

Fig 1.5 *Demonstration of the force between adjacent parallel current-carrying conductors*

flowing in circular coils show the same effect, i.e. currents in neighbouring coils flowing in the same direction attract, and currents flowing in opposite directions repel.

The Rayleigh current balance, the principle of which is shown in fig 1.6, consists of an outer pair of fixed flat coils with a movable flat coil hung coaxially between the fixed coils from the right-hand scale pan of a sensitive balance. The coils are connected so that the same current flows through the three coils, the directions being such that the force on the movable coil is initially a downward one. Masses are added to the left-hand scale pan to restore balance. The

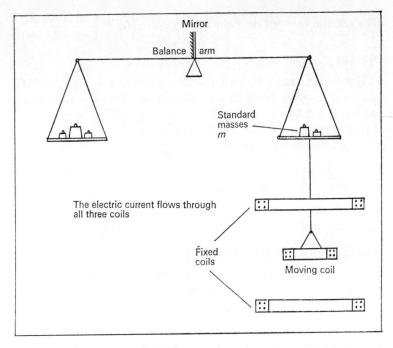

Fig 1.6 *A current balance is used to determine the ampere*

current in the fixed coils is then reversed and standard masses of total mass *m*, exerting a total downward force *mg*, are placed on the right-hand scale pan to restore balance once again. The current is then determined by this latter force and a knowledge of the dimensions of the coils. Such a current balance is equivalent to a parallel conductor arrangement and achieves an accuracy of about 4 parts in 100 000.

Having chosen the unit of electric current as the basic electrical unit, the unit of electric charge is now defined in terms of it as follows: 'The coulomb is the quantity of electric charge transported in one second by a current of one ampere'; i.e. for steady currents, the relation between these physical quantities is

$$\text{charge } (Q) = \text{current } (I) \times \text{time } (t)$$

or
$$I = \frac{Q}{t} \tag{1.2}$$

The relation between the units is 1 ampere (A) $= \dfrac{1 \text{ coulomb (C)}}{1 \text{ second} \quad \text{(s)}}$.

Worked Example

How many electrons, each carrying a charge $e = 1\cdot6 \times 10^{-19}$ C, drift past a given point in a conductor in 1 s, when the electric current is 1 A?

Let N electrons flow past the point in 1 s.

Charge transported $Q = N e$ but $Q = I t$

hence $N = \dfrac{I t}{e} = \dfrac{1 \times 1}{1\cdot6 \times 10^{-19}} = 6\cdot25 \times 10^{18}$

i.e. 6 250 000 000 000 000 000 electrons drift past a given point in a conductor in 1 s, when the current is 1 A.

Drift Velocity of Electrons

How do the free electrons move in a metal such as copper? Is it possible to construct a simple model of their motion which does not conflict with accepted theories such as the Kinetic Theory and

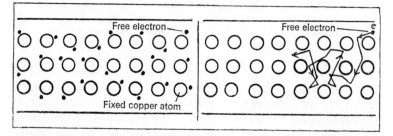

Fig 1.7 *A crude 'atomic scale' view of copper atoms in a wire with their free electrons*

Fig 1.8 *A steady drift superimposed on the random motion of a free electron in a metal*

Quantum Theory? Any attempt to construct such a model is bound to be somewhat crude, because electron motion in metals cannot be observed experimentally. However, a simple picture such as fig 1.7 is useful at this stage. On such an 'atomic scale', the copper atoms are in a regular lattice, and each atom vibrates about its average position. The outer electron of each atom is able to move freely from one atom to another, this motion being extremely rapid and quite haphazard. Calculations indicate an average electron speed of the order of 300 km s^{-1}, 1/1000 of the velocity of light. One can imagine that at any one instant, say one million electrons are travelling from left to right across a very thin section of copper wire, and one million electrons are effectively travelling from right to left. There is a frantic movement of electric charge across the thin section, but there is no *resultant* transfer of charge across the section and hence no electric current is detected.

If, however, more electrons are urged to cross the section in one particular direction, then there is a net drift of electric charge across the section and a direct current is detected. This drift is superimposed on the rapid random motion of the electrons (seen in fig 1.8), and it is possible to derive an expression for the drift velocity v_d in terms of the current I and other known or measurable quantities.

Relation between Drift Velocity of Electrons and Electric Current

Let there be n free electrons per unit volume, each carrying a charge e, in a conductor of cross-sectional area A and length l (see fig 1.9).

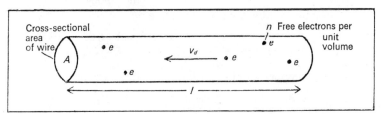

Fig 1.9 *Electron drift velocity v_d in a metallic conductor*

Number of free electrons in length $l = n\,A\,l$

Total electric charge $\qquad\qquad Q = (n\,A\,l)\,e$

Suppose this charge Q contained in length l of the conductor passes through the end section A in time t with drift velocity v_d

then $\qquad\qquad v_d = l/t \quad \text{or} \quad t = l/v_d$

$\therefore$ current $\qquad\qquad I = \dfrac{Q}{t} = \dfrac{n\,A\,l\,e}{l/v_d}$

$\qquad\qquad \therefore\ I = n\,A\,e\,v_d$

$\qquad\qquad \therefore\ v_d = \dfrac{I}{n\,A\,e}.$ $\qquad\qquad$ (1.3)

15

Worked Example

Estimate the drift velocity of free electrons in 26 s.w.g. copper wire carrying a current of 3 A, assuming each copper atom contributes one free electron.

Given:

diameter of 26 s.w.g. wire $d = 4 \cdot 57 \times 10^{-4}$ m
density of copper $= 8 \cdot 90 \times 10^3$ kg m^{-3}
charge on electron $e = 1 \cdot 60 \times 10^{-19}$ C

Avogadro constant $N_A = 6 \cdot 02 \times 10^{23}$ mol^{-1}
Molar mass of copper $= 0 \cdot 064$ kg mol^{-1}

To determine the number of free electrons per unit volume n:

Mass of copper per unit volume
$$= 8 \cdot 90 \times 10^3 \text{ kg m}^{-3}$$

$\therefore$ number of moles per unit volume
$$= 8 \cdot 90 \times 10^3 \frac{\text{kg}}{\text{m}^3} \times \frac{1}{0 \cdot 064} \frac{\text{mol}}{\text{kg}}$$

$\therefore$ number of atoms per unit volume
$$= \frac{8 \cdot 90 \times 10^3}{0 \cdot 064} \frac{\text{mol}}{\text{m}^3} \times \frac{6 \cdot 02 \times 10^{23}}{\text{mol}}$$

Since each copper atom contributes one free electron
$$n = \frac{8 \cdot 90 \times 6 \cdot 02 \times 10^{26}}{0 \cdot 064} \frac{\text{electrons}}{\text{m}^3}$$

$\therefore n = 8 \cdot 37 \times 10^{28}$ electrons m^{-3}

To calculate the cross-sectional area of the wire A:
$$A = \frac{\pi d^2}{4} = \frac{\pi \times (4 \cdot 57 \times 10^{-4})^2}{4} = 1 \cdot 64 \times 10^{-7} \text{ m}^2$$

To evaluate the drift velocity v_d:
$$v_d = \frac{I}{n A e} \quad \text{(see equation 1.3)}$$

$\therefore \quad v_d = \dfrac{3}{8 \cdot 37 \times 10^{28} \times 1 \cdot 64 \times 10^{-7} \times 1 \cdot 60 \times 10^{-19}}$

$$= 1 \cdot 37 \times 10^{-3} \text{ m s}^{-1}$$

$\therefore \quad$ drift velocity $= 1 \cdot 4$ mm s^{-1}

i.e. it takes an electron on average just over 7 seconds to drift one centimetre in 26 s.w.g. copper wire when the current is 3 A. This slow drift velocity should be compared with the rapid thermal velocity of electrons which is of the order of 300 km s^{-1}.

Potential Difference, the Volt

Before the idea of electrical potential difference (p.d.) is introduced, it is useful to look at the analogous case of gravitational potential difference.

The difference in gravitational potential between two points is defined as the work done in transferring unit mass from one point to the other. Suppose a brick is carried up a ladder, then work is done against the gravitational pull of the earth on the brick. If the brick falls back to its original level, the acquired potential energy changes to kinetic energy which is then dissipated mainly in the form of heat energy.

The exact parallel is seen in the electrical case. The difference in electrical potential between two points is defined as the work done in taking unit charge from one point to the other. Suppose a quantity of charge has its potential changed within a cell by the conversion of chemical energy, and the charge drifts back to its original poten-

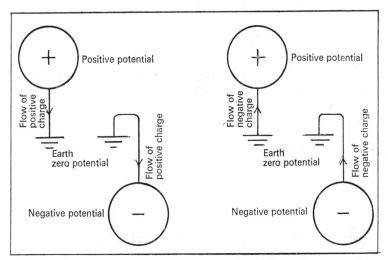

Fig 1.10 *Positive charge flows from high positive potential to a lower potential; negative charge flows towards a higher and more positive potential*

tial level, through an external circuit, then the acquired electrical energy changes to kinetic energy of the charge carriers, which in turn lose their energy by collisions, causing a heating effect. The direction of motion of positive charge or conventional electric current is taken to be from a high positive potential to a lower potential. Since electrons are the charge carriers in metals, and since electrons carry a negative charge, their motion is always from a low to a higher positive potential. The earth itself is taken as the zero of electrical potential, and if a wire connection is made between earth and a positively charged insulated conductor, electrons move from earth to neutralise the positive charge (see fig 1.10). This flow of charge can be detected on a sensitive suspended coil light beam galvanometer. Similarly, electrons flow from a conductor at a negative potential to earth via a wire connection.

The definition of the unit of p.d. follows from the definition of electrical potential difference:

The p.d. between two points is 1 volt if 1 joule of work is done in transferring 1 coulomb of charge from one point to the other.

e.g. if 6 J of work is done in transferring 3 coulombs of charge from one point to the other, then the p.d. between the two points is

$$\frac{6\,J}{3\,C} = 2\,\frac{J}{C} = 2\,V$$

i.e.
$$1 \text{ volt (V)} = \frac{1 \text{ joule (J)}}{1 \text{ coulomb (C)}}.$$

An alternative way of defining the volt is in terms of the ampere (coulomb/second) and watt (joule/second):

The p.d. between two points of a conducting wire is 1 volt if 1 watt of power is dissipated between the points when the constant current is 1 ampere

i.e.
$$1 \text{ volt (V)} = \frac{1 \text{ watt (W)}}{1 \text{ ampere (A)}}$$

or
$$\text{amps} \times \text{volts} = \text{watts}.$$

Calibration of Ammeter and Voltmeter

Any simple current balance may be used as a local basis for defining the ampere. In such a local current balance (fig 1.11), the coils and standard mass have been adjusted during construction so that the current which just restores balance after the standard mass has been placed on the scale pan agrees, for convenience, with 1 ampere. Ideally, of course, such a balance should be checked against one of the standard balances kept at a Standards Laboratory, but this is rarely a practical proposition.

Using the simple 'standard' balance, the 1 ampere calibration is checked on several ammeters; alternately, the scale on the ammeters

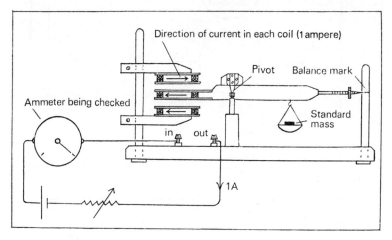

Fig 1.11 *One ampere is the current which just restores balance after the standard mass has been placed on the scale pan. The 1 ampere deflection on the ammeter is being checked*

is covered with a strip of paper, the zero is marked and a 1 A marking is made where the pointer of the ammeter settles when the current balance indicates that one ampere is flowing. Both methods emphasise the fact that the definition of the ampere only indicates what is meant by 1 ampere; the definition does not indicate what is meant by 2 amperes or any multiple or sub-multiple of 1 ampere.

To calibrate (or check) an ammeter X in one-ampere intervals, several ammeters whose 1 ampere calibration has been checked using the local standard balance, are arranged as shown in fig 1.12. The basic principle used is that electric charge is conserved and does not build up at any particular point in a circuit. These facts are expressed in Kirchhoff's first law: the total current entering a junction in a circuit equals the total current leaving the junction. Hence when

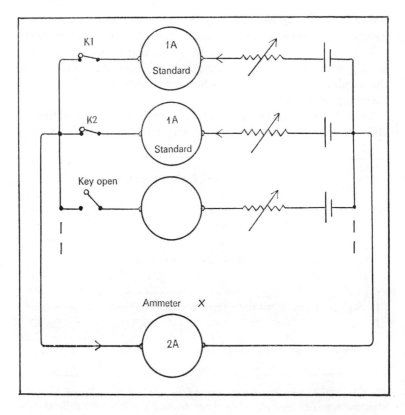

Fig 1.12 *Calibration of ammeter using several ammeters whose 1 ampere calibration has been checked using a local current balance*

keys K1 and K2 are depressed and the ammeters in these branches indicate 1 ampere, then the current flowing through ammeter X is 2 amperes, and so on. It is left to the student to design a similar experiment to calibrate ammeter X in sub-multiples of an ampere.

A method for the *absolute* determination of the magnitude of an electric current in amperes is available and will be described when the necessary theory has been studied. But for the initial work on the magnetic effect of an electric current, an ammeter will be used which has been calibrated against a current balance and by Kirchhoff's first law.

A voltmeter can now be calibrated as a direct application of the definition of the volt as a joule per coulomb, i.e. a p.d. (in volts) V

exists between two points if work W (in joules) is done in transferring electric charge Q (in coulombs) between the points, such that

$$V = W/Q$$
$$\therefore W = Q V. \qquad (1.4)$$

Using $Q = I t$ (equation 1.2), electrical energy $W = V I t$.

The principle of the calibration is to connect the voltmeter across a heating coil, and to obtain values for the energy expended (W in joules) in pushing electric charge (Q in coulombs) through the heating coil. The potential difference across the coil is defined by W/Q in joule coulomb^{-1}, and that is the reading in volts to be marked on the blank scale of the meter. The charge Q equals the product of the current I times the time t for which it flows in the heating coil, but how can the energy expended W be measured? It is fortunate that both electrical energy and mechanical energy can be wholly transformed into heat energy, and that the latter can be measured by the temperature rise produced by the heat in, say, a metal cylinder. Electrical and mechanical energy are measured in joules, and a preliminary experiment is done to find the mechanical energy M which is required to raise the temperature of the metal cylinder by 1 K. By the law of conservation of energy, M is also the amount of electrical energy required to raise the temperature of the metal cylinder by 1 K, in fact, M is the heat capacity of the cylinder in joule kelvin^{-1}. If, therefore, current I flowing for time t through the above heating coil embedded in the metal cylinder causes a temperature rise of θ_e, then the electrical energy expended must have been $W = M \times \theta_e$.

Preliminary mechanical experiment: The metal cylinder is mounted so that it can be turned about a horizontal axis by a handle. A heavy mass m (~ 8 kg) is attached to a nylon cord which is wound round the circumference of the cylinder until there are sufficient turns (~ 6) for the frictional force to raise the mass slightly off the floor when the handle is turned steadily. The other end of the nylon cord is attached to a fixed rubber band and this should be just slack. A thermometer is put in the cylinder, and the initial temperature is recorded. The cylinder, of diameter d, is then turned N times (~ 150) against the tension in the cord $= mg$, g being the gravitational field strength $= 9\cdot8$ newton kilogramme^{-1}. The maximum temperature reached by the cylinder is recorded. Let the temperature rise be θ_m (~ 10 K), then the mechanical energy expended to raise the temperature of the cylinder through 1 K is given by

$$M = \frac{mg \times \pi d \times N}{\theta_m} \text{ (in J K}^{-1}\text{)}.$$

Electrical experiment: The metal cylinder, with the same number of turns of nylon cord wound round it as before, is now placed on a stand so that electrical contact can be made with the ends of the heating coil. The voltmeter to be calibrated is connected in parallel with the coil, and a calibrated ammeter and a variable 12 V d.c. supply is connected in series with the coil (see fig 1.13). A steady current is passed through the heating coil, a trial having given the magnitude of the current which raises the temperature of the metal cylinder by approximately the same amount as in the mechanical

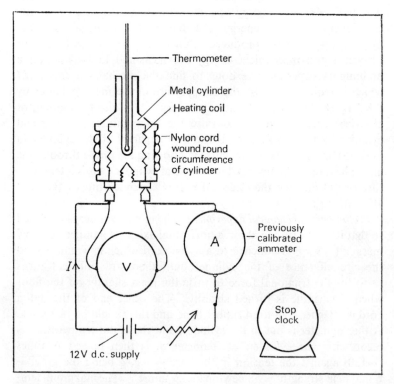

Fig 1.13 *Principle of the calibration of a voltmeter, using the already calibrated ammeter (see fig 1.12)*

experiment, and in about the same time. This precaution ensures that the heat losses are similar in the two experiments and that they can be neglected. Suppose the resultant temperature rise is θ_e. This has been caused by a transformation of energy $M \times \theta_e$ = electrical energy W. The quantity of electric charge $Q = I \times t$. Hence the voltmeter connected across the coil should register

$$\frac{W}{Q} = \frac{M\,\theta_e}{I\,t} \text{ (in volts)}.$$

It should be noted that 1 calorie of heat energy is now *defined* to be *exactly* 4·1868 joule, and that the unit of heat energy is the joule. Hence heat capacity is expressed in $J\,K^{-1}$.

Resistance, the Ohm

Is there a relationship between the p.d. V maintained across the ends of a metallic conductor and the current I flowing in the conductor? Simple measurements, using the circuit shown in fig 1.14, with an ammeter and voltmeter calibrated as described in the previous section, indicate that the ratio V/I has a constant value, called the *resistance R* of the metallic conductor.

Hence $\qquad\qquad\qquad V/I = R \qquad\qquad\qquad$ (1.5)

This equation, known as Ohm's law, holds for a metallic conductor

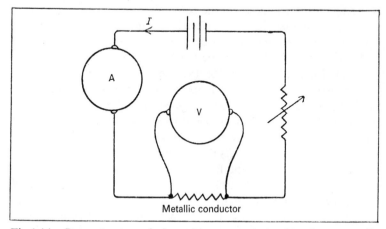

Fig 1.14   *Determination of the p.d./current relationship for a metallic conductor, with an ammeter and voltmeter calibrated previously*

provided its physical condition remains unaltered during an experiment.

It should be noted that for all non-metals and for metals whose physical condition changes during the experiment the ratio $\dfrac{V}{I} = R$ does not remain constant. Equation (1.5) defines resistance.

The unit of resistance is the ohm, this being the resistance of a conductor through which a current of 1 ampere passes when a p.d. of 1 volt is maintained across its ends

i.e. $$1 \text{ ohm } (\Omega) = \frac{1 \text{ volt (V)}}{1 \text{ ampere (A)}}.$$

Questions

1. An electric charge is made up of an integral number of a tiny quantum of charge e, which has a magnitude of $1 \cdot 60 \times 10^{-19}$ coulomb. How was the evidence for this statement accumulated at the beginning of the twentieth century?

2. Explain carefully how you would demonstrate the existence of
   (a) two, and only two, types of electric charge,
   (b) a conservation law for electric charge.

3. Describe and explain two experiments which serve to establish the identity of static and current electricity.   (L. part)

4. Define (a) the ampere, (b) the coulomb.

Do you consider the unit of electric current or the unit of electric charge to be the more fundamental? Give reasons.

Which unit was chosen to be the basic unit of electricity in the 'Système International d'Unités' (SI), and why?

5. An electric current of $0 \cdot 3$ ampere flows in a torch bulb for 10 seconds. What is (a) the total charge which has passed through the filament, (b) the number of electrons which have drifted past a given point in the filament? (Electronic charge $e = 1 \cdot 60 \times 10^{-19}$ C.)

6. Summarise very briefly (i) the physical similarities, (ii) the physical differences between the flow of an electric current (a) along a wire, (b) through an electrolyte, (c) through a gas. (Theories of conduction are not required.)

A metal wire of cross-section 1 mm^2 carries a direct current of 1 A. Assuming that there are 10^{23} electrons per cm^3 of metal which can move freely through the metal, and that the charge on an electron is 1.6×10^{-19} coulomb, calculate the mean velocity of motion of the electrons. If a 50 Hz sinusoidal alternating current of r.m.s. value 1 A flows in the same wire, calculate the maximum velocity of the electrons and their amplitude of oscillation.　(S.)

7. Explain qualitatively how electrical resistivity can be understood on the basis of the movement of electrons through a solid.

A 50 Hz (cycles per second) alternating current of magnitude 10 A (r.m.s.) passes along a copper wire whose diameter is 1 mm. If copper contains 9×10^{22} free electrons per cm^3 what is the amplitude of the displacement of the electrons in the copper associated with the current? (Charge on the electron = 1.6×10^{-19} coulomb.)

A wire of length l and resistance R is extended by an amount ε such that $\varepsilon \ll l$. If the volume of the wire and its resistivity remain unchanged what is the fractional change in R?

If $R = 100$ ohms and $\varepsilon/l = 0.001$ suggest a method of measuring the change in R.　(O. & C. Special)

8. Which of the following quantities

charge $\times$ time^{-1}; energy $\times$ charge^{-1}; force $\times$ distance;
p.d. $\times$ current^{-1}; force $\times$ distance $\times$ time^{-1}

represent

(a) work;　(b) power;　(c) p.d.;
(d) current;　(e) resistance?

Supply units for each as in the following example:

force (newtons) = mass (kilogrammes) $\times$ acceleration (metres second^{-2}).　(S.C.E. part)

9. Define　(a) the joule　(b) the volt
Justify that 'watts = amps $\times$ volts'.

How many joules of energy are transformed in the element of a 1 kilowatt electric fire in 1 hour? If the current flowing is 4 amperes (i) what is the potential difference across the element, (ii) how many coulombs of electric charge have drifted through the above element in 1 hour?

10. Describe an experiment you would set up to demonstrate Ohm's law, explaining carefully the basis for the calibration of any electrical measuring instrument whose readings you assume to be correct showing that this has not involved any assumption of the law. Give two examples of classes of conductors which follow Ohm's law and two which do not.　(S. Special part)

Chapter 2

The Magnetic Field of an Electric Current

Magnetic Field Patterns

The year was 1819. Professor Oersted was giving a lecture on the simple cell to a group of students at the University of Copenhagen. When Oersted connected a conducting wire across the cell, he noticed that a pivoted magnetic compass needle, which happened to be near the wire, became slightly deflected. When he disconnected the wire from the cell, the compass needle returned to its original position. Oersted had made a discovery, which, as we now know, has had far-reaching consequences: *An electric current sets up what is called a 'magnetic field' in the space surrounding the current-carrying conductor.* In such a region, a force is exerted on magnetic materials and other current-carrying conductors. What is the pattern of such a magnetic field near differently shaped current-carrying conductors? What is a useful model by which a magnetic field can be visualised?

Magnetic Field due to a Current in a Straight Conductor

A straight, vertical conducting wire is inserted through a small hole in a stiff white card, supported horizontally. An electric current, of the order of 6 A, is switched on and small iron filings (preferably magnetised by having held the 'pepper pot dispenser' near a strong magnet) are sprinkled on the card which is tapped gently with a pencil. The iron filings form themselves into a pattern of concentric circles about the wire. A small magnetic plotting compass placed on the card shows that when the current is reversed in the conductor, the direction of the magnetic field is reversed at a given point (see fig 2.1). The lines in fig 2.1, whose shapes are such that a plotting compass always sets itself tangentially to them, are called *lines of*

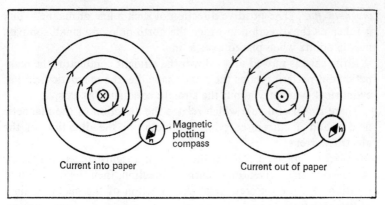

Fig 2.1 *Magnetic field due to an electric current in a straight conductor*

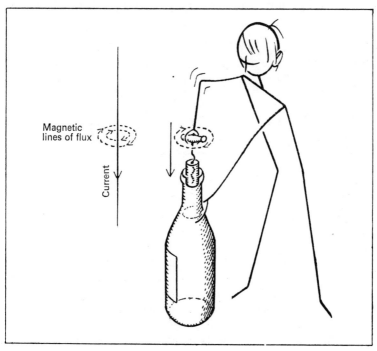

Fig 2.2 *Maxwell's Corkscrew Rule; relates the direction of the magnetic field to the direction of the electric current*

27

magnetic flux. The positive direction of such a line of magnetic flux is taken as the direction in which the north pole of a small compass needle points when placed over a line.

If the card is moved up or down the straight conductor, the magnetic field pattern retains the same shape, i.e. the magnetic field has cylindrical symmetry about the straight conductor as axis.

There is a useful rule which relates the direction of the magnetic field round a current-carrying conductor to the direction of the electric current.

Maxwell's Corkscrew Rule: If the point of a right-handed corkscrew is moved in the conventional current direction, then the direction of rotation of the corkscrew gives the direction of the magnetic lines of flux (see fig 2.2).

Magnetic Field due to a Current in a Circular Coil

A circular coil of about twenty turns of closely wound copper wire (say 26 s.w.g., p.v.c. covered) is threaded through two holes in a

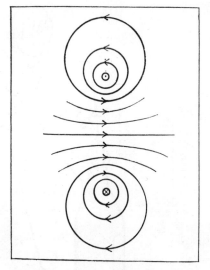

Fig 2.3 *Magnetic field due to an electric current in a circular coil*

horizontal card so that the card bisects the coil. The largest safe current is passed through the coil. Fig 2.3 shows the pattern of the magnetic flux lines, which indicate that the direction of the magnetic field at the centre of the coil is at right angles to the plane of the coil. It should be noted that if the direction of a physical quantity, e.g. electric current, is into the paper, this is represented by $\otimes$; if the direction is out of the paper, this is represented by $\odot$.

Magnetic Field due to a Current in a Solenoid

A closely wound solenoid is made of dimensions similar to those of a short permanent bar magnet (e.g. Alnico or Alcomax). The pattern of the magnetic field is investigated with iron filings and a small

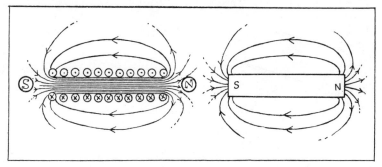

Fig 2.4 *Magnetic field of current-carrying solenoid and bar magnet of similar dimensions*

plotting compass inside and around the current-carrying solenoid, and around the bar magnet. The similarity (see fig 2.4) between the magnetic field patterns of the current-carrying solenoid (and coil) and the short permanent magnet is a striking one.

The polarities of the ends of a current-carrying coil or solenoid are readily predicted by the following 'Clock Rule': When viewing one end of the coil or solenoid, if the current is in an aNticlockwise direction (N), that end acts like a N pole; if the current is in a clockwise direction (S), that end acts like a S pole.

A current-carrying solenoid, which is freely suspended horizontally in the earth's magnetic field, sets itself along the magnetic meridian at that point in the same way as the magnetic needle of a plotting compass. Magnetic flux lines representing the earth's magnetic field over a small area at a particular place on earth are effectively parallel. Parallel lines of magnetic flux are a feature of a uniform magnetic field.

Force on a Current-carrying Conductor in a Uniform Magnetic Field

Newton's third law states the following: 'To every action force there is an equal and opposite reaction force.' If this idea is applied to Oersted's discovery that a current-carrying conductor causes an unbalanced force to act on a pivoted magnetic needle until the needle sets itself tangential to a magnetic flux line, then it is reasonable to predict that a uniform magnetic field will exert a force on a

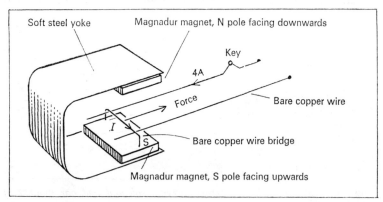

Fig 2.5 *The 'Catapult Experiment' illustrates the force on a current-carrying conductor in a magnetic field*

current-carrying conductor, unless the conductor lies parallel to the magnetic lines of flux.

An investigation of this hypothesis is illustrated in fig 2.5. A short length of bare copper wire (e.g. 26 s.w.g.) is placed with its ends turned down as a bridge over two parallel and horizontal rails of bare copper wire. The 'bridge' is placed perpendicular to a strong uniform magnetic field and a current (e.g. 4 A) is passed through the bridge conductor, which immediately catapults along the rails. Maximum force is observed under these conditions. No force is observed, however, when the current-carrying bridge conductor is parallel to the magnetic field, which confirms the hypothesis. This leads to an alternative definition of the direction of a magnetic field —it is the direction in which a current-carrying conductor element placed in the magnetic field experiences no force. The positive direction of the magnetic field is then deduced by applying Fleming's Left-Hand Rule, which is essentially a summary of experimental observa-

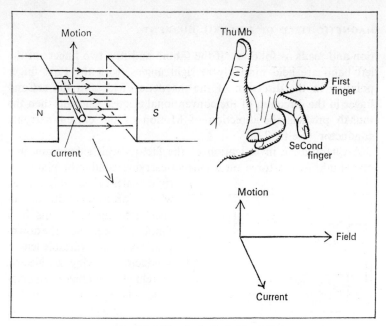

Fig 2.6   *Fleming's Left-Hand Rule*

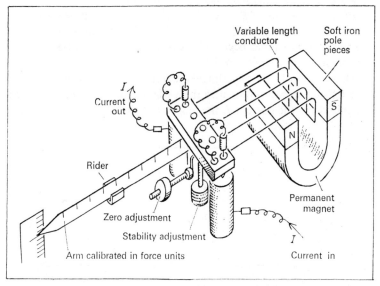

Fig 2.7   *The 'Force-on-Conductor Balance' is used to investigate the relationship between the force on a current-carrying conductor and the magnitude of the current, and the length of the conductor, in a uniform magnetic field*

tion and reads as follows: 'If the thumb and first two fingers of the left hand are held mutually at right angles, with the First finger pointing in the direction of the magnetic Field, and the seCond finger in the direction of the conventional electric Current, then the thuMb predicts the direction of Motion of the current-carrying conductor' (see fig 2.6).

A quantitative investigation of the factors which determine the magnitude of the force on a current-carrying conductor placed at right angles to the field, is made with a 'Force-on-conductor balance' (see fig 2.7). This is a simple balance, where the downward force on a variable length conductor carrying an electric current at right angles to a magnetic field, is measured by sliding a rider along the opposite arm of the balance which is graduated in force units. The electric circuit is shown in fig 2.8. The current is measured on an ammeter which has been calibrated using a 'Current balance' and Kirchhoff's first law (see p. 19).

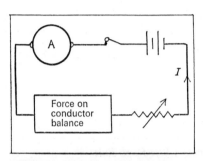

Fig 2.8 *Electric circuit for the experimental deduction of F = B I l*

The results of two experiments are shown graphically in fig 2.9. The left-hand graph illustrates the variation of the force F with the magnitude of the current I, the length l of the conductor being kept

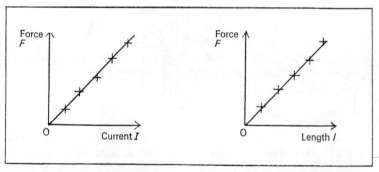

Fig 2.9 *The results show that the force on a current-carrying conductor is proportional to the current flowing and the length of the conductor*

constant. The right-hand graph shows the variation of F with l, I being kept constant.

Both graphs are straight lines passing through the origin

$$\therefore \quad F \propto I$$

$$\text{and} \quad F \propto l$$

$$\therefore \quad F \propto I\,l.$$

During both experiments, the third possible variable, i.e. the magnetic field in air, was kept constant. Hence, when the above proportionality is expressed as an equation, the constant of proportionality, for which the symbol B is chosen, must involve the magnitude of the magnetic field

$$\text{i.e.} \quad F = B\,I\,l \tag{2.1}$$

where force F is in newtons
current I is in amperes
length l is in metres.

Magnetic Flux Density, *B*

The equation $F = B\,I\,l$ is used to define B, which is given the name 'magnetic flux density', and which is a measure of the strength of a magnetic field.

Definition: 'The magnetic flux density B is numerically equal to the force per unit length experienced by unit current which is at right angles to the magnetic field.'

It follows from this definition that B is a vector quantity, i.e. it has magnitude and direction, the direction at any point being that of the positive direction of the magnetic line of flux at that point. The magnitude of B, measured by the force on unit length of current, may be represented by the number of magnetic flux lines which pass through unit area; the greater the number of lines per unit area, the greater is the strength of the magnetic field.

Rearranging equation 2.1 gives

$$B = F/I\,l. \tag{2.2}$$

The unit of B is derived by combining the units on the right-hand side of this equation.

$$\frac{N}{A\,m} = \frac{N}{A\,m} \times \frac{m}{m} = \frac{J}{A\,m^2} = \frac{A\,V\,s}{A\,m^2} = \frac{Wb}{m^2} = T(\text{tesla})$$

33

Definition: 'A magnetic flux density of 1 tesla causes a force of 1 newton per metre length on a current of 1 ampere flowing at right angles to the magnetic field.' It should be noted that the unit name *tesla* is the derived SI unit for magnetic flux density B; the most useful alternatives are *newton per ampere metre* and *weber per metre²*.

Determination of Magnetic Flux Density B using a 'Force on Conductor' Balance

The electric circuit is set up as before (see fig 2.8), with the length l of conductor placed at right angles to the magnetic flux density B and the current I in such a direction, that the force F exerted on the current-carrying conductor can be balanced by moving a rider along the opposite arm of the balance, which is graduated in force units. The force is measured for five values of the current, and the results plotted on a force versus current graph (like the left-hand graph in fig 2.9).

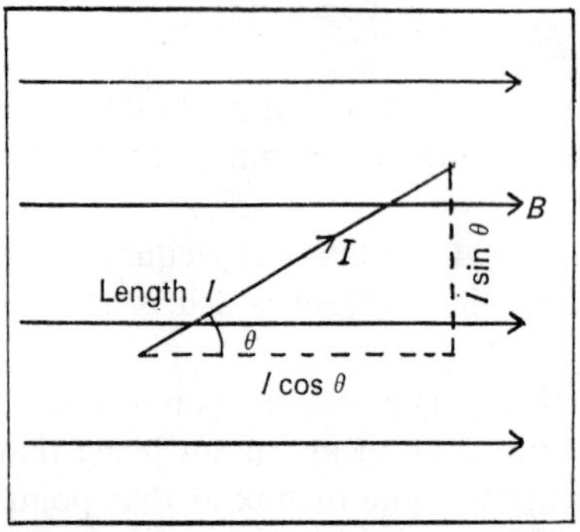

Fig 2.10 *The effective length of conductor perpendicular to B is l sin θ. The force is F = B I l sin θ into the paper*

By comparing $F = B\,I\,l$ with the equation of a straight line which passes through the origin, $y = m\,x$, it is seen that the gradient of the F versus I graph is $B\,l$. Hence $B = $ gradient$/l$, l being the measured length of the current-carrying conductor.

Worked Example

Calculate the magnetic flux density of a magnetic field in which a 4 cm length of conductor carrying a current of 2 A and inclined at 30° to the field experiences a force of $3{\cdot}32 \times 10^{-3}$ N.

Given: current $I = 2$ A

effective length $l \sin \theta = 4 \times 10^{-2} \times \sin 30° = 2 \times 10^{-2}$ m

force $F = 3{\cdot}32 \times 10^{-3}$ N

Using $F = B\,I\,l \sin \theta$ (see fig 2.10)

$$B = \frac{3{\cdot}32 \times 10^{-3}}{2 \times 2 \times 10^{-2}} = 8{\cdot}3 \times 10^{-2} \text{ T}$$

For comparison, the horizontal component of the earth's magnetic flux density $= 1\cdot8 \times 10^{-5}$ tesla.

Force on an Electric Charge moving in a Uniform Magnetic Field

Suppose a charge Q contained in a length l of a conductor passes through the end section of cross-sectional area A in time t with drift velocity v_d

then $\qquad t = l/v_d$

and current $\qquad I = \dfrac{Q}{t} = \dfrac{Q\,v_d}{l}.$

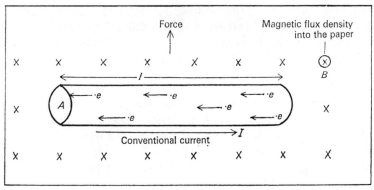

Fig 2.11   *The force $F = B\,I\,l$ is the resultant of all the forces on all the electrons moving with drift velocity v_d in the conductor length l*

If the conductor is at right angles to a uniform magnetic field of magnetic flux density B (shown acting into the paper in fig 2.11) then the force acting on the conductor is given by equation (2.1).

$$F = B\,I\,l.$$

Substituting $\qquad F = B\,\dfrac{Q\,v_d}{l}\,l$

i.e. $\qquad F = B\,Q\,v_d.$

Let the charge Q be made up of N electrons each of charge e

then $\qquad F = B\,Ne\,v_d.$

35

Hence the average force on a *single* electron, moving in a metallic conductor with average drift velocity v_d at right angles to a magnetic flux density B, is given by

$$F = B\,e\,v_d. \tag{2.3}$$

If the electron is moving with constant speed v in a vacuum at right angles to a magnetic flux density B, then the force on the electron is given by

$$F = B\,e\,v. \tag{2.4}$$

Such a constant force, always acting at right angles to the electron path, causes a circular electron orbit.

Returning to equation 2.3, one can see now that the force $B\,I\,l$ on a current-carrying conductor in a magnetic field is the *resultant* of all the forces on all the electrons moving with drift velocity v_d. When using Fleming's Left-Hand Rule, it should be noted that negative charges moving from right to left are equivalent to conventional current flowing from left to right (see fig 2.11).

Worked Example

Calculate the force F on an electron charge $e = 1 \cdot 60 \times 10^{-19}$ C moving with drift velocity $v_d = 1 \cdot 37 \times 10^{-3}$ m s^{-1} in a copper wire which is at right angles to a field of magnetic flux density 0·1 tesla. (Note: The quoted drift velocity is that of electrons in 26 s.w.g. copper wire carrying a current of 3 A—see Worked Example, p. 16.)

Now $\qquad F = B\,e\,v_d$ (equation 2.3)

$\therefore \quad F = 10^{-1} \times 1 \cdot 60 \times 10^{-19} \times 1 \cdot 37 \times 10^{-3}$

$\therefore \quad F = 2 \cdot 19 \times 10^{-23}$ N.

Taking the mass of an electron as $9 \cdot 1 \times 10^{-31}$ kg, and its weight as

$$9 \cdot 1 \times 10^{-31} \times 9 \cdot 8 \text{ N} = 8 \cdot 92 \times 10^{-30} \text{ N, then}$$

$$\text{the force on the electron} = \frac{2 \cdot 19 \times 10^{-23}}{8 \cdot 92 \times 10^{-30}}$$

$= 2 \cdot 46 \times 10^{6}$ greater than the weight of the electron.

Torque on a Flat, Pivoted Coil in a Uniform Magnetic Field

Fig 2.12 shows a pivoted rectangular coil of sides length a and b (in metres), which can rotate about a vertical axis YY'. Suppose this flat

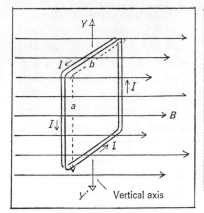

Fig 2.12 *A pivoted current-carrying coil tends to rotate in a magnetic field until the normal to the plane of the coil is parallel to the lines of flux*

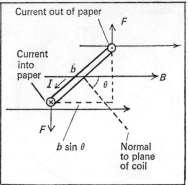

Fig 2.13 *Two equal and opposite forces F tend to rotate the coil. This is a plan view of fig 2.12*

coil has N turns, and that the normal to the plane of the coil makes an angle θ with a magnetic field of magnetic flux density B (in teslas).

When a current I flows in the coil in the direction shown, a force acts on each of the four sides of the rectangular coil. Applying Fleming's Left-Hand Rule, the top and bottom of the coil are acted on by forces which tend to stretch the coil. However, the vertical sides of the coil are acted on by two equal and opposite forces F (see fig 2.13), which tend to rotate the coil about the vertical axis YY'.

Since the sides of the coil are perpendicular to the magnetic flux density, the magnitude of the force on N lengths a is given by

$$F = BINa.$$

Now Torque (T) = Force $(F) \times$ perpendicular distance between the two forces ($b \sin \theta$)

$$\therefore \quad T = F \times b \sin \theta$$

$$\therefore \quad T = BINab \sin \theta.$$

As ab is the cross-sectional area of the coil A in metres^2,

$$T = BINA \sin \theta. \tag{2.5}$$

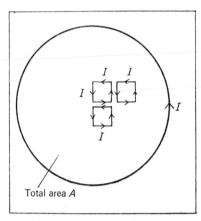

Fig 2.14 *A circular coil of area A may, in theory, be replaced by an infinite number of small current loops of total area A*

It can be shown that equation 2.5 holds for *any* flat coil of area *A*. As example, consider a circular coil carrying a current *I*. Its area can be replaced by an infinitely large number of small rectangular or square current loops of total area *A* with current *I* flowing round each small rectangular loop in the same direction as in the circular coil (see fig 2.14). Forces on the sides of the rectangular current loops cancel at all points except on the circular boundary, which is now considered to be made up of an infinite number of small steps.

Hence the torque on a circular coil, or indeed any flat coil, is given by equation 2.5.

Electromagnetic Moment of a Coil, Solenoid and Permanent Bar Magnet

The maximum torque T_{max} on a flat coil of N turns and cross-sectional area A carrying a current I is exerted when the plane of the coil is parallel to the external magnetic flux density B, and hence $\theta = 90°$ and $\sin \theta = 1$ in equation 2.5.

$$\therefore \quad T_{max} = B\,I\,N\,A$$

The product $I \times A$ is called the *electromagnetic moment* of a single current loop, with derived unit ampere metre², and $I \times N\,A$ is the electromagnetic moment m of a current loop with N turns.

Hence
$$m = \frac{T_{max}}{B}. \tag{2.6}$$

Electromagnetic moment m is defined from equation 2.6.
Definition: The electromagnetic moment of a coil is numerically equal to the torque per unit applied magnetic flux density, when the central axis of the coil is perpendicular to the applied magnetic flux density (see fig 2.15). Electromagnetic moment is a vector quantity,

its direction being along the axis of a current loop, i.e. perpendicular to the area of a loop. The positive direction of the electromagnetic moment vector is the same as the positive direction of the axial magnetic flux density *due* to the current loop. It is useful to think of the torque on a current loop always trying to line up the electro-

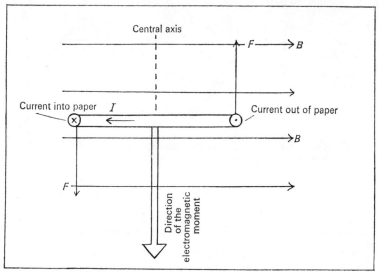

Fig. 2.15 *Plan view of a current loop. The electro magnetic moment of the loop = area of loop × current flowing round loop = ratio of maximum torque to applied magnetic flux density B*

magnetic moment vector of the loop with the direction of the applied magnetic flux density vector (see fig. 2.16).

The equivalence of the magnetic field patterns of a current-carrying solenoid and a bar magnet has already been established (see fig 2.4), and so it is not surprising that the action of an applied magnetic field on a freely suspended current-carrying solenoid or bar magnet should be similar (see fig 2.17 and fig 2.18).

Again using equation 2.6, $m = \dfrac{T_{\max}}{B}$, *the definition of m becomes:*

The electromagnetic moment of a current-carrying solenoid or bar magnet is numerically equal to the torque per unit applied magnetic flux density, when the central axis of the solenoid or magnet is perpendicular to the applied magnetic flux density. Again it should be noted that the torque in fig 2.17 and fig 2.18 tries to line up the electromagnetic moment vector with the direction of the applied magnetic flux density vector.

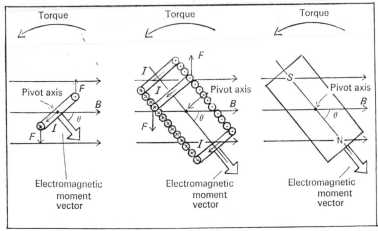

Fig 2.16   Fig 2.17   Fig 2.18

A comparison of the torque on a single current loop, a current-carrying solenoid, and a permanent bar magnet, in a uniform applied field of magnetic flux density B

Sensitivity of Moving-coil Galvanometer with Radial Field

An important practical application of the torque on a current-carrying coil in a magnetic field is in the moving-coil galvanometer. In order that the torque is a maximum whatever the position of the current-carrying coil, the coil moves over a soft iron cylinder between the concave pole pieces of a permanent magnet (see fig 2.19), which produces a radial magnetic field. The forces F, acting on the vertical sides of the coil of mean area A moving in this radial field of magnetic flux density B, are always at right angles to the coil, thus producing a constant maximum torque. The coil settles in a deflected equilibrium position, when the deflecting torque due to the current I in the coil equals the restoring torque of the hair springs. This restoring torque can be shown by experiment to be proportional to the angular deflection α (in radians) of the hair springs.

Let the restoring torque be c (in newton–metre per radian). If the coil turns through α to its equilibrium position, then

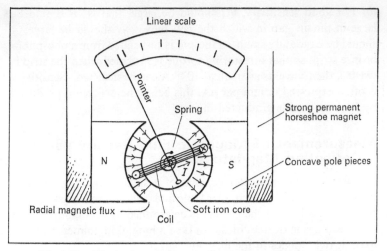

Linear scale

Pointer

Spring

Strong permanent
horseshoe magnet

N S

Concave pole pieces

I

Radial magnetic flux

Coil

Soft iron core

Fig 2.19 *The basic components of a moving-coil galvanometer*

deflecting torque = restoring torque

$$\therefore \quad BINA = c\,\alpha.$$

Hence the deflection per unit current, which is termed the sensitivity of the galvanometer, becomes

$$\frac{\alpha}{I} = \frac{BNA}{c}. \tag{2.7}$$

Unit check:

Left-hand side of equation 2.7: $\dfrac{\text{rad}}{\text{A}}$

Right-hand side of equation 2.7:

$$\frac{\text{N}}{\text{A}\,\text{m}} \times \text{m}^2 \times \frac{\text{rad}}{\text{N}\,\text{m}} = \frac{\text{rad}}{\text{A}}$$

An inspection of equation 2.7 leads to some important conclusions:
(*a*) For a given galvanometer, the deflection α is proportional to the current I flowing in the coil, hence providing a linear scale (as shown in fig 2.19). This enables one to convert the instrument into an ammeter by using a suitable low resistance shunt, or into a voltmeter by using a suitable high resistance multiplier.

(b) For good sensitivity, α/I should be large, that is: B should be large in the air gap in which the coil moves, N should be large, A should be large and c small. If the coil is suspended from a phosphor-bronze strip, so that a restoring torque is provided when the strip is twisted, then currents as small as 10^{-9} A can be detected. Sensitivity is often expressed in mm per μA, this being the deflection produced by 1 μA on a scale graduated in mm.

Measurement of Magnetic Flux Density using a Deflection Magnetometer

A deflection magnetometer consists of a small magnet, pivoted at the centre of a movable circular scale and enclosed in a glass-topped box. The position of the magnet is determined by averaging the two scale readings in degrees of the ends of a long, thin pointer, which is fixed at right angles to the magnet.

The horizontal component B_x of the earth's magnetic flux density will exert a torque on the horizontally pivoted magnet and will deflect it into the magnetic meridian. The ends of the pointer should

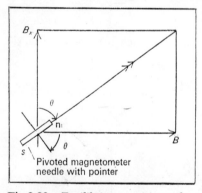

then be over the zero marks on the circular scale. The direction of the magnetic flux density B of unknown magnitude is now arranged to be at right angles to the magnetic meridian. The pivoted magnet is deflected through an angle θ from the magnetic meridian and settles along the direction of the resultant magnetic flux density (see fig 2.20).

Pivoted magnetometer needle with pointer

Fig 2.20 *Equilibrium position of a small pivoted magnet under the influence of two perpendicular magnetic flux densities B_x and B*

In fig 2.20 $\quad \tan \theta = \dfrac{B}{B_x}$

$$\therefore \quad B = B_x \tan \theta. \quad (2.8)$$

Hence the actual value of B is given by equation 2.8, if B_x is known. Since B_x is constant at a particular place, certainly for the duration of an experiment, it follows that the numerical value of $\tan \theta$ is directly proportional to the magnitude of the magnetic flux density B being investigated.

Investigation of Factors causing B at the Centre of a Circular Coil

What physical quantities cause the magnetic flux density B to have a particular value at some point near a current-carrying conductor? Any configuration of conductor can be chosen for an experimental investigation, however, the results using a circular coil, lead easily to the important 'Biot–Savart' equation (see p. 46) and for that reason the circular coil is preferred to the straight conductor or solenoid.

The design of the apparatus for this experiment, as indeed for any experiment in physics, depends largely on the hypothesis, i.e. on the intelligent guess which is made regarding the factors which are likely to affect the quantity under investigation. Magnetic field pattern experiments with a simple circular coil, iron filings and small magnetic plotting compasses (see p. 28), lead to the hypothesis that B at the centre of a circular coil is most likely affected by

(*a*) the current I

(*b*) the length l of the conductor (related to the number of turns N)

(*c*) the radius r of the coil.

The direction of B at the centre of a current-carrying circular coil, is known; it is perpendicular to the plane of the coil (see fig 2.3) Hence a deflection magnetometer can be used to determine B in terms of $\tan \theta$, as explained on p. 42.

A suitable apparatus for the experiment is shown in fig 2.21. A vertical wooden board carries concentric circles of thin dowel pegs. At the centre of the circles is a platform for the deflection magnetometer. It is clear looking at part (*c*) of the hypothesis that a *constant* length l of conducting wire should always give a whole number of turns N on any one of the concentric circles, so that the variation of B with r can be investigated. This is achieved by ensuring

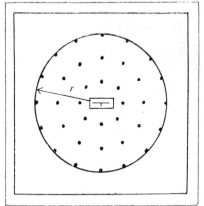

Fig 2.21 *Pegboard showing three of the six concentric circles of pegs, with the deflection magnetometer in the centre of the vertical board*

43

that the product $r N$ (or $2\pi r N$) is constant. Table 2.1 suggests suitable values for r, used in the design of the peg-board, corresponding to integral values of N.

Radius of coil r (metre)	Number of turns N
0·20	3
0·15	4
0·12	5
0·10	6
0·075	8
0·060	10

Table 2.1

Values of r used in the design of the peg-board shown in fig 2.21. The product $r N$ is constant.

The peg-board is placed with its plane in the magnetic meridian, and about 4 metres of insulated copper wire (e.g. 26 s.w.g.) is connected in series with a variable d.c. supply and a 'calibrated' ammeter. In part (a), l and r are kept constant by wrapping a whole number of turns round one of the circles of pegs, and the deflection θ of the magnetometer needle is noted for at least five values of I. The graph of $\tan \theta$ ($\propto B$) versus I is a straight line passing through the origin (see fig 2.22(a)), hence $B \propto I$. In part (b), I and r are kept constant, θ being measured for at least five different lengths of conducting wire on a particular circle of pegs. The graph of $\tan \theta$ versus l is also a straight line passing through the origin (see fig 2.22(b)), hence $B \propto l$.

For part (c), I and l are kept constant, a whole number of turns

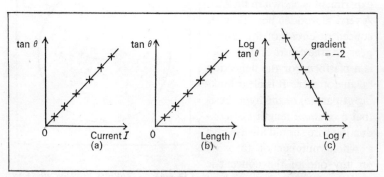

Fig 2.22 *The results show that the magnetic flux density at the centre of a circular coil is proportional to the current, the length of the conductor in the coil, and inversely proportional to the square of the radius of the coil*

being wound on each circle according to table 2.1. A plot of $\tan \theta$ versus r is inconclusive; however, the graph of $\log (\tan \theta)$ versus $\log r$ is a straight line with gradient $= -2$ (see fig 2.22(c)). So

$$B \propto \frac{1}{r^2}.$$

From the combined results,

$$B \propto \frac{Il}{r^2}.$$

A fourth possible variable, i.e. a property of the medium (air), stayed constant during the experiments. When the above proportionality is expressed as an equation, the constant of proportionality, for which the form $\mu/4\pi$ is chosen, must be a function of the medium. μ is called the permeability of the medium.

$$\text{i.e.} \quad B = \frac{\mu}{4\pi} \frac{Il}{r^2}. \tag{2.9}$$

The factor 4π is written into the formula because SI units are a rationalised system of units. The factor 4π appears in formulae with spherical symmetry, 2π appears in formulae with cylindrical symmetry, and no π's appear in formulae with plane symmetry. It follows, therefore, that the magnitude of μ depends not only on the medium, but also on the system of units employed. The derived unit for μ is

$$\frac{\text{N m}^2}{\text{A m A m}} = \frac{\text{V s}}{\text{A m}} = \frac{\text{H}}{\text{m}} \text{ or } \frac{\text{henry}}{\text{metre}},$$

the henry being 1 volt-second per ampere.

The Biot–Savart Equation and Derived Formulae

A situation sometimes arises in physics where a hypothesis is made of a relationship between physical quantities which cannot be verified by direct experiment. If, however, the *deductions* made from the hypothesis are verifiable, then the original hypothesis is accepted as a law. Such an example is the Biot–Savart equation, often called the Biot–Savart law, which states the following: Consider a very short length of conductor δl carrying a steady current I (the product $I \, \delta l$ is known as a current element). Then the contribution of this current element to the magnetic flux density at a point P (into the paper) distance r from the current element (see fig 2.23), when the line from P to the current element makes an angle θ with it in an isotropic* medium of permeability μ, is given by

$$\delta B = \frac{\mu \, I \, \delta l \sin \theta}{4\pi \, r^2}. \tag{2.10}$$

This is the Biot–Savart equation.

In order to obtain an expression for the magnetic flux density at a point near a current-carrying conductor, it is therefore necessary

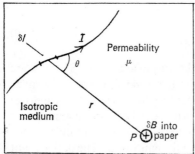

Fig 2.23 *The current element $I\delta l$, in the plane of the paper, makes angle θ with the line, length r, joining it to point P*

$$\delta B = \frac{\mu I \delta l \sin \theta}{4\pi r^2}$$

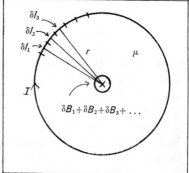

Fig 2.24 *The total magnetic flux density due to all the current elements in the circumference is given by*

$$B = \Sigma \frac{\mu \, I \delta l \sin \theta}{4\pi r^2}$$

to sum the contributions $\delta B_1 + \delta B_2 + \delta B_3 + \ldots = $ total B due to the current elements $I \, \delta l_1, I \, \delta l_2, I \, \delta l_3, \ldots$ into which the current-carrying conductor may be divided.

The resemblance between the experimentally derived equation 2.9 and the Biot–Savart equation 2.10 is a striking one, and, of course, equation 2.9 should follow as a deduction from the Biot–Savart equation.

* Isotropic—having uniform physical properties in all directions.

Magnetic Flux Density at the Centre of a Circular Coil

Suppose a circular coil radius a, with N turns, has a steady current I flowing in it. If the coil is divided into current elements, then each is a distance a from the centre C of the coil, and the line, i.e. radius, joining the current element to C makes angle $\theta = 90°$ with the current element (see fig 2.24). The magnetic flux density B at the centre is the sum of the terms δB for the current elements.

$$B = \sum \frac{\mu I \, \delta l \sin \theta}{4\pi \, r^2}$$

Now $r = a, \sum \delta l = l$, the total length of the coil $2\pi a N$, and $\sin \theta = 1$, since $\theta = 90°$

$$\therefore \quad B = \frac{\mu I l}{4\pi a^2} \quad \text{(which is like equation 2.9).}$$

Substituting $2\pi a N$ for l and rearranging,

$$B = \mu \frac{N}{2a} I. \tag{2.11}$$

The direction of B may be deduced by applying the 'Clock Rule' (see p. 29).

Other important formulae, which may be checked by experiment, will now be derived from the Biot–Savart equation.

Magnetic Flux Density at a Point P on the Axis of a Circular Coil

Consider a circular coil of N turns, radius a, carrying a current I and situated in an isotropic medium of permeability μ. Suppose the plane of the coil is perpendicular to the plane of the paper (see fig. 2.25). Dividing the coil into current elements, each one is at right angles ($\theta = 90°$) to the line, length r, joining the current element to point P and making an angle α with the axis PC. The direction of the vector δB due to the current element $I \, \delta l$ shown in fig 2.25, is at right angles to the line, length r, and is in the plane of the paper.

$$\delta B = \frac{\mu I \, \delta l}{4\pi \, r^2}$$

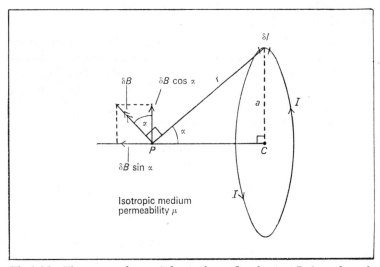

Fig 2.25 *The current element $I\delta l$ contributes flux density $\delta B \sin \alpha$ along the axis of the circular coil at P*

δB is now resolved into a component $\delta B \sin \alpha$ along the axis, and a component $\delta B \cos \alpha$ perpendicular to the axis. If current elements at opposite ends of a diameter of the circular coil are considered, then the magnetic flux density components perpendicular to the axis cancel. Each current element will contribute a component $\delta B \sin \alpha$ to the total magnetic flux density B at point P, the direction of B being along the axis (compare with fig 2.3)

$$\therefore \quad B = \sum \frac{\mu \, I \, \delta l \sin \alpha}{4\pi \, r^2}$$

but $\sum \delta l = 2\pi \, a \, N$ and $\sin \alpha = a/r$

$$\therefore \quad B = \frac{\mu \, I \, 2\pi \, a \, N}{4\pi \, a^2} \sin^3 \alpha$$

$$\therefore \quad B = \mu \frac{N}{2a} I \sin^3 \alpha. \qquad (2.12)$$

Equation 2.12 reduces to equation 2.11 when point P coincides with the centre of the circular coil. Then $\alpha = 90°$ and $\sin^3 \alpha = 1$.

48

Magnetic Flux Density at a Perpendicular Distance from a Long, Straight Conductor

Consider the small current element $I\,\delta l$, distance r from P (see fig 2.26), which contributes magnetic flux density δB at point P, into the paper. P is at a perpendicular distance a from the infinitely long straight conductor carrying a current I in an isotropic medium of

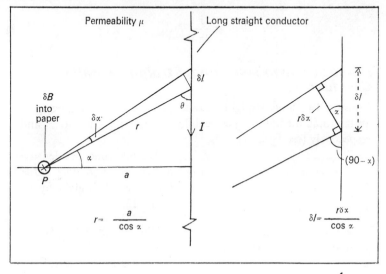

Fig 2.26 *The total magnetic flux density at P is given by* $B = \mu\,\dfrac{1}{2\pi a}\,I$

permeability μ. Let the current element subtend angle $\delta\alpha$ at P, and let the angle which the line of length r makes with $I\,\delta l$ be $(90 - \alpha)°$

$$\therefore \quad \delta B = \frac{\mu\,I\,\delta l \sin(90-\alpha)}{4\pi\,r^2}$$

but $\sin(90-\alpha) = \cos\alpha$ and from fig 2.26,

$$\delta l = \frac{r\,\delta\alpha}{\cos\alpha} \quad \text{and} \quad r = \frac{a}{\cos\alpha}$$

by substitution,

$$\delta B = \frac{\mu\,I}{4\pi\,a}\cos\alpha\,\delta\alpha.$$

49

The total magnetic flux density at P due to all the current elements making up the long, straight conductor is obtained by integrating the above expression over all angles of α from $-\dfrac{\pi}{2}$ to $+\dfrac{\pi}{2}$

$$\therefore \quad B = \frac{\mu I}{4\pi a} \int_{-\pi/2}^{+\pi/2} \cos \alpha \, d\alpha$$

$$\therefore \quad B = \mu \frac{1}{2\pi a} I. \tag{2.13}$$

Force between Two Long, Straight, Parallel Conductors

Consider two long, straight, parallel conductors, distance a apart in an isotropic medium of permeability μ, carrying currents I_1 and I_2 respectively (see fig 2.27).

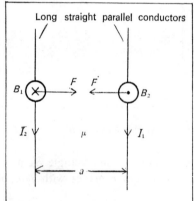

Long straight parallel conductors

The magnetic flux density B_1 at the second conductor due to the current I_1 is given by equation 2.13.

i.e. $\quad B_1 = \mu \dfrac{1}{2\pi a} I_1.$

Neglecting the earth's magnetic field, the second conductor lies in this particular flux density and the force per metre exerted on it is given by equation 2.1

i.e. $\quad \dfrac{F}{l} = B_1 I_2$

$$\therefore \quad \frac{F}{l} = \mu \frac{I_1 I_2}{2\pi a}. \tag{2.14}$$

Fig 2.27 *The force per unit length between the straight, parallel conductors is given by* $\dfrac{F}{l} = \mu \dfrac{I_1 I_2}{2\pi a}$

Both conductors experience this force per unit length, attractive in the case of currents flowing in the same direction.

This last equation is a very important one. The definition of the ampere is based on it, and the value of the permeability of free space μ_0 is deduced from it. Referring to the definition (p. 10),

$$I_1 = I_2 = 1 \text{ A}$$

$$a = 1 \text{ m}$$

$$F/l = 2 \times 10^{-7} \text{ N m}^{-1}$$

and the isotropic medium is vacuum, with permeability μ_0.
Substituting in equation 2.14,

$$2 \times 10^{-7} = \mu_0 \frac{1 \times 1}{2\pi \times 1}$$

$$\therefore \quad \mu_0 = 4\pi \times 10^{-7} \text{ H m}^{-1}.$$

Thus the value of μ_0 follows from the definition of the ampere in the SI units.

Magnetic Flux Density on the Axis of a Solenoid

Consider a solenoid, radius a, having N/l turns per metre of its length, and carrying a current I. To calculate the magnetic flux density at a point P on the axis of the solenoid situated in an isotropic medium of permeability μ, the solenoid may be thought to be made up of a large number of flat circular coils placed side by side, the width of the coil being δl (see fig 2.28).

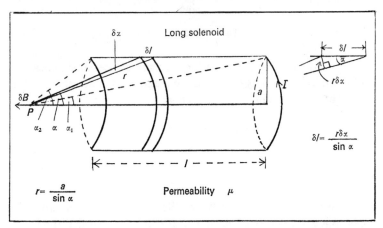

Fig 2.28   *The total magnetic flux density at P is given by*

$$B = \tfrac{1}{2}\mu \frac{N}{l} I (\cos \alpha_1 - \cos \alpha_2)$$

Now in fig 2.28, $\sin \alpha = \dfrac{r\,\delta\alpha}{\delta l}$ $\quad \therefore \quad \delta l = \dfrac{r\,\delta\alpha}{\sin \alpha}.$

The number of turns in length δl is $\dfrac{N}{l} \times \delta l = \dfrac{N}{l} \times \dfrac{r\,\delta\alpha}{\sin \alpha}.$

The magnetic flux density at P due to a circular coil of width δl is given by equation 2.12,

$$\delta B = \mu\,\frac{N I}{2a}\sin^3 \alpha$$

$$\therefore \quad \delta B = \mu\,\frac{\dfrac{N}{l}\dfrac{r\,\delta\alpha}{\sin \alpha}\,I}{2a}\,\sin^3 \alpha \qquad \text{but } r = \frac{a}{\sin \alpha}$$

hence $\qquad \delta B = \tfrac{1}{2}\mu\,\dfrac{N}{l}\,I \sin \alpha\,\delta\alpha$

in the direction shown in the diagram.

The total magnetic flux density at P due to all the 'coil elements' is obtained by integrating the above expression over all angles of α from α_1 to α_2

$$\therefore \quad B = \tfrac{1}{2}\mu\,\frac{N}{l}\,I \int_{\alpha_1}^{\alpha_2} \sin \alpha\,\mathrm{d}\alpha$$

$$\therefore \quad B = \tfrac{1}{2}\mu\,\frac{N}{l}\,I\,(\cos \alpha_1 - \cos \alpha_2). \tag{2.15}$$

Two particular cases of equation 2.15 are of special significance. (a) For an infinitely long solenoid, the magnetic flux density near the middle of the solenoid is given when $\alpha_1 = 0$, $\alpha_2 = \pi$

$$\therefore \quad B = \tfrac{1}{2}\mu\,\frac{N}{l}\,I\,(1+1)$$

$$B = \mu\,\frac{N}{l}\,I. \tag{2.16}$$

A solenoid does not have to be infinitely long for this equation to apply to a good degree of accuracy. It can be shown that the value for B near the centre of an ordinary solenoid only varies by $\tfrac{1}{2}\%$ from the value for an infinitely long solenoid, provided the length is approximately $10 \times$ the diameter of the solenoid.

(b) If P is at the end of a long solenoid, then $\alpha_1 = 0$, $\alpha_2 = \pi/2$

$$\therefore \quad B = \tfrac{1}{2}\mu \frac{N}{l} I (1-0)$$

$$B = \tfrac{1}{2}\mu \frac{N}{l} I. \tag{2.17}$$

A comparison of the value of B at the end, and at the centre of a long solenoid, shows that the 'Biot–Savart equation deduction' predicts that B at the end has half the value of B at the centre.

Absolute Determination of the Ampere

The word 'absolute' does not mean that the determination is made with supreme accuracy, but that the unit is calculated in terms of the basic units, i.e. the metre, kilogramme and second. In the case of the absolute determination of an electrical unit, e.g. the ampere,

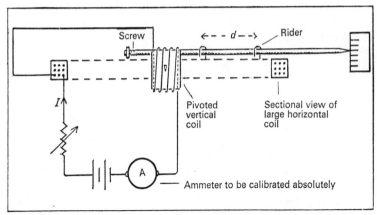

Fig 2.29 *Principle of a method for the 'absolute' determination of the ampere using a simple current balance*

the property of the medium in which the experiment takes place is also involved. In the experiment to be described, the permeability of air is assumed equal to μ_0, the permeability of free space. Actually μ for air $= 1\cdot000\ 000\ 38 \times \mu_0$, so the approximation is well justified.

A suitable apparatus (fig 2.29) consists of a small, pivoted, vertical

53

coil of N_2 turns and cross-sectional area A, which is at the centre of a larger, fixed, horizontal coil of N_1 turns and mean radius a. The current I which is to be determined, flows through both coils in series, entering and leaving the pivoted coil at the pivots.

The magnetic flux density at the centre of the large coil is given by equation 2.11.

$$B = \mu_0 \frac{N_1}{2a} I.$$

So the deflecting torque on the pivoted coil is (equation 2.5)

$$T = B\, I\, N_2\, A$$

$$\therefore \quad T = \mu_0 \frac{N_1\, N_2\, A\, I^2}{2a}.$$

The restoring torque is provided by moving a small rider of mass m a distance d along a pointer arm attached to the pivoted coil. If g is the gravitational field strength then the restoring torque $= m\, g\, d$.

For equilibrium $\quad \mu_0 \dfrac{N_1\, N_2\, A\, I^2}{2a} = m\, g\, d$

$$\therefore \quad I = \sqrt{\frac{2a \times m\, g\, d}{\mu_0\, N_1\, N_2\, A}}.$$

A convenient method for the experiment is as follows:

(1) The pivoted coil is adjusted with its pointer opposite the zero of the scale, with the rider in its zero position.

(2) A current of 1 ampere, as registered on an ammeter, is passed through the pivoted coil only.

A small deflection is obtained, which is neutralised by adjusting a screw on the pointer. The effect of the earth's magnetic field has been eliminated.

(3) The coils are now connected in series and the low voltage d.c. supply is adjusted so that 1 ampere flows through both coils.

(4) The rider is moved through a distance d (a few cm) until the pointer is again restored to its zero position.

(5) The rider is weighed on a chemical balance (mass $\simeq$ 50 mg). Typical result: Value of current determined absolutely using the formula, $I = 1\cdot02$ A; value indicated on the ammeter $= 1\cdot0$ A.

The ammeter, which was calibrated arbitrarily against a local current balance and then by Kirchhoff's first law (see p. 19), can now be calibrated absolutely.

Questions

(Take $g = 9\cdot81$ m s^{-2} = $9\cdot81$ N kg^{-1}.)

1. What do you understand by a line of magnetic flux (force)?

Using the model of magnetic lines of flux (force), differentiate between uniform, non-uniform and radial magnetic fields.

State rules which relate the magnetic field direction and electric current direction in
   (a) a straight conductor
   (b) a solenoid.

2. Sketch the distribution of magnetic flux (force) lines for
   (a) a magnetic compass needle (alone)
   (b) the earth's field over a small area in a horizontal plane
   (c) a horizontally pivoted magnetic compass needle in equilibrium in the earth's magnetic field.

Comment on any special features in each sketch.

3. Describe suitable experiments which lead to the relation $F = B I l$, where F is the force in newtons on a conductor of length l in metres carrying a current I in amperes at right angles to a uniform magnetic flux density B in teslas.

State 'Fleming's Left-Hand Rule', which relates the directions of F, B and $(I l)$ in the above equation.

4. Define magnetic flux density B and derive a suitable unit for B in SI units.

A straight conductor carries a current of $2\cdot5$ amperes perpendicular to a magnetic flux density of $0\cdot05$ tesla. Calculate the force per unit length on the conductor in newton metre^{-1}.

What is the force on the conductor if it is inclined at 30° to the field?

5. Derive an expression for the force F acting on a charge e moving at right angles to a magnetic field of flux density B with speed v.

What perpendicular force is exerted in a uniform magnetic field of flux density $0\cdot1$ tesla on

(a) 10^{10} electrons drifting in a conductor with a velocity of 1 mm s^{-1},

(b) 1 electron moving in a vacuum with a velocity of 10^7 m s^{-1}. Comment on the results. (electronic charge = 1.6×10^{-19} C.)

6. Show that if a free electron moves at right angles to a magnetic field the path is a circle. Show also that the electron suffers no force if it moves parallel to the field. Point out how the steps in your proof are related to fundamental definitions.

If the path of the electron is a circle, prove that the time for a complete revolution is independent of the speed of the electron.

In the ionosphere electrons execute 1.4×10^6 revolutions in a second. Find the strength of the magnetic induction (flux density) in this region.

Mass of an electron = 9.1×10^{-31} kg; electronic charge = 1.6×10^{-19} coulomb. (C. Special)

7. An electron with a velocity of 10^7 m s^{-1} enters a region of uniform magnetic flux density of 0.10 tesla the angle between the direction of the field and the initial path of the electron being 25°. By resolving the velocity of the electron find the axial distance between two turns of the helical path. Assume that the motion occurs in a vacuum and illustrate the path with a diagram. ($e/m = 1.8 \times 10^{11}$ coulomb kg^{-1}) (J.M.B. Special)

8. A square coil of side 0.20 m lies in a magnetic field of flux density 0.5 tesla so that the plane of the coil makes an angle of 60° with the field lines. Find the torque exerted on the coil if it carries a current of 0.25 A. (Assume $N = 1$ turn.) (B.Ed. Edinburgh part)

9. Define electromagnetic moment.

A magnetised uniform rod of length 0.15 m is pivoted about a horizontal axis passing through its centre of mass. The axis of rotation is perpendicular to a uniform magnetic field of flux density 8.0×10^{-5} tesla inclined at 60° to the horizontal. When a small mass of 0.20 g is fixed to one end of the rod, the rod sets horizontally.

Draw a diagram to show the couples acting on the rod in this position. Calculate the electromagnetic moment of the rod.

(J.M.B. adapted)

10. Describe, with diagrams, the structure of a sensitive moving coil galvanometer. Without detailed mathematical analysis explain what factors control the sensitivity.

A galvanometer of resistance 100 ohm is shunted by a resistance of 1·0 ohm. The combination is connected in series with a resistance of 10^4 ohms and an accumulator of e.m.f. 2·0 V and negligible internal resistance. What is the sensitivity of the galvanometer if it shows a deflection of 20 divisions? (A.E.B. part)

11. The Biot–Savart equation is

$$\delta B = \frac{\mu I \, \delta l \sin \theta}{4\pi \, r^2} \quad \text{(using the usual symbols).}$$

Explain, with the aid of a clearly labelled sketch, the meaning of this equation, and state a consistent set of units for each physical quantity.

Apply the equation to the case of a circular conducting loop and derive the expression for the magnetic flux density B at the centre of the loop.

12. A flat, circular coil of 6 turns, situated in air, has a radius of 10 cm. What current is required to produce a magnetic flux density at its centre, equal to that of the earth's horizontal component of $1·8 \times 10^{-5}$ tesla. (Assume the permeability of air $= \mu_0 = 4\pi \times 10^{-7}$ H m^{-1}.)

13. A current-carrying vertical wire produces a neutral point with the earth's horizontal component of $1·8 \times 10^{-5}$ tesla at a distance of 5 cm from the wire. Calculate the value of the current flowing. (Take $\mu_0 = 4\pi \times 10^{-7}$ H m^{-1}.)

14. Deduce an expression for the strength of the magnetic flux density B generated by a current I flowing in a long straight wire, at a point distant a from it.

State clearly the electrical principles you assume as the basis for your deduction and discuss the experimental evidence on which you accept them. To what accuracy would you estimate that the principles are known to be true?

A long straight wire is fixed so as to run close to a diameter of a circular coil of single turn, which is free to move, but makes no contact with the straight wire. A current of 10 amperes flows through both. Determine the nature and magnitude of any force or couple which is experienced by the circular coil and their dependence, if any, on the radius of the circular coil.

Could you design a current-measuring device based upon this arrangement? Indicate any advantages it would possess.

(S. Special adapted)

15. By starting with any general relation between a current and the magnetic flux density due to it, derive an expression for the magnetic flux density at any point, due to a current in a long straight wire. How would you verify by experiment the relation between magnetic flux density and the distance from the wire?

Two long parallel straight wires are set up vertically in a plane at right angles to the magnetic meridian, with their axes 10 cm apart. The wires carry, in the same direction, equal currents of 12·0 amperes. Find the positions of neutral points in any horizontal plane. (Take the horizontal component of the earth's magnetic flux density $= 1·8 \times 10^{-5}$ T.) (L.)

16. Define the term 'neutral point in a magnetic field'.

Draw the magnetic field associated with two parallel wires placed a short distance apart and carrying the same current in the same direction. Mark the position of any neutral points.

Describe with the aid of a sketch the working of a moving-coil galvanometer or ammeter. How does the design ensure a uniform scale?

A horizontal electric cable is in the plane of the magnetic meridian and carries a current of 500 amperes in the N–S direction. If the horizontal component of the earth's field is $1·7 \times 10^{-5}$ tesla and the angle of dip is 67°, what is the magnitude and direction of the force on a 100 m length of cable? (S.C.E. adapted)

17. A 1000-turn air-cored solenoid, 50 cm long, carries a current of 1 ampere. Calculate the magnetic flux density B along the axis
    (a) at the centre of the solenoid,
    (b) at either end of the solenoid.

Given that the diameter of the solenoid is 6 cm, calculate the magnitude of B at a point along the axis 25 cm outside the solenoid. (Assume the permeability of air $= \mu_0 = 4\pi \times 10^{-7}$ H m^{-1}.)

18. Define electromagnetic moment.

A small magnet, suspended with its axis horizontal so as to be able to rotate freely about a vertical axis, is situated at the centre of a long horizontal solenoid, the axis of which lies at right angles to the magnetic meridian. If the solenoid has 20 turns per cm, determine the value of the current passing through it which would cause the magnet to rotate through 50°. (Take the horizontal component of the earth's magnetic flux density = $1·8 \times 10^{-5}$ tesla and $\mu_0 = 4\pi \times 10^{-7}$ H m^{-1}.) (J.M.B. adapted)

19. Show that a charged particle moving with constant speed at right angles to a uniform magnetic field in a vacuum travels in a circular path and find an expression for the time taken to complete one revolution.

What is the path of a charged particle in a uniform magnetic field if its initial velocity is not at right angles to the field?

An electron of speed 2×10^7 m s^{-1} is emitted from a point on the axis of a very long solenoid wound with 10 turns per cm and carrying a current of 2·5 A. If the initial velocity makes an angle α with the solenoid axis, find at what distance from its starting point the particle next crosses the axis, and show that this distance is almost independent of α if α is small. (e/m for electron = $1·76 \times 10^{11}$ coulomb kg^{-1}; $\mu_0 = 4\pi \times 10^{-7}$ henry m^{-1}) (O. & C. Special)

20. A circular coil of radius 15 cm was mounted with its plane horizontal and another circular coil of 100 turns each of radius 2 cm was pivoted at its centre so that it could turn about a diameter of the large coil. The small coil carried a light counterbalanced pointer fixed at right angles to its plane. The coils were connected in series and a current passed through them. A rider of mass 0·04 g was adjusted on the pointer to keep the plane of the small coil vertical. The following results were obtained for d, the distance from rider to pivot and N, the number of turns in the large coil:

d in cm	14·7	13·4	12·0	10·6	9·3	8·0
N	100	90	80	70	60	50

Represent these results graphically and use the graph to calculate the current in the coils and the strength of the earth's vertical component.

State clearly any formulae used in the calculation, and list the probable sources of error in this experiment. (S.)

Chapter 3

Electromagnetic Induction

Magnetic Flux, ϕ

After Oersted's accidental discovery in 1819 that a magnetic field is set up in the space surrounding a current-carrying conductor, scientists began to search for a method by which a magnetic field might induce a current to flow in a conductor. After repeated failure, success came in 1832, when Faraday in England and Henry in America announced independently that relative motion between a magnetic field and a conductor causes a current to flow in the conductor. Faraday went on to construct the first dynamo, the forerunner of the giant electric generator of the twentieth century.

Faraday was also the first to use the concept of lines of magnetic flux to help him picture and explain the effects he had discovered. The student is already familiar with the properties of magnetic flux lines. In the case of uniform magnetic fields, for example, the magnetic flux lines are parallel and equally spaced, and in a strong field, the lines are more tightly bunched than in a weak field. Thus, in a quantitative study of uniform magnetic fields, a large number of magnetic flux lines passing at right angles through a given area represent a large magnetic flux density B. It follows that the magnetic flux lines themselves can be considered to be a measure of what is called 'magnetic flux' ϕ. A magnetic flux density B (in teslas) is produced by a magnetic flux ϕ passing at right angles through an area A in metre^2. This is summarised by the equation

$$B = \frac{\phi}{A} \tag{3.1}$$

and it will be clear that the unit of magnetic flux is the weber.

If the magnetic field is not uniform, then the magnetic flux density at a point in the field is the limiting value of $\delta\phi/\delta A$, where $\delta\phi$ is the magnetic flux passing normally through a tiny area δA drawn around

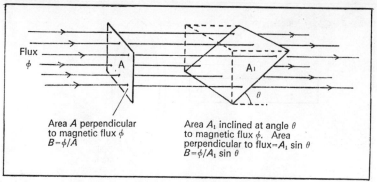

Area A perpendicular
to magnetic flux ϕ
$B = \phi/A$

Area A_1 inclined at angle θ
to magnetic flux ϕ. Area
perpendicular to flux=$A_1 \sin \theta$
$B = \phi/A_1 \sin \theta$

Fig 3.1   *The relationship between uniform flux ϕ, magnetic flux density B, and perpendicular area A is B = ϕ/A*

the point. As $\delta A \to 0$, the magnetic flux density at the point is given by

$$B = \frac{\mathrm{d}\phi}{\mathrm{d}A}. \qquad (3.2)$$

If magnetic flux passes through (or threads) an area A_1 which is inclined at angle θ to the direction of the flux (see fig 3.1), then the area presented normally to the flux is $A_1 \sin \theta$ and $B = \dfrac{\phi}{A_1 \sin \theta}$.

Lenz's Law of Electromagnetic Induction

Two simple experiments illustrate the basic principles of electromagnetic induction.

Induced e.m.f. due to Relative Motion between a Conductor and a Magnetic Field

When the N pole of a small permanent magnet is moving into a coil of about 20 turns of conducting wire connected to a sensitive centre-zero galvanometer (fig 3.2), a deflection is observed (to the right, say), indicating that a current is being induced in the coil. A similar deflection is obtained if the coil is moved towards the N pole of the permanent magnet. When the N pole is moved away from the coil, or the S pole into the coil, the deflection is in the opposite direction (to the left). An induced current only flows when there is relative motion between the coil and magnet; the faster the relative motion, the greater the induced current.

Now an induced current can only have been caused to flow by an

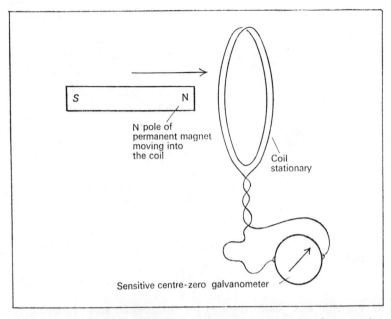

Fig 3.2 *An 'induced' current flows in the coil when there is relative motion between the coil and the magnet*

induced voltage, i.e. by a momentary seat of electromotive force (e.m.f.) in the wire. The induced e.m.f. in fig 3.3 can have been caused either by a change in the total number of magnetic flux lines *threading* the coil, or by the wires of the coil *cutting* across the flux lines of the magnetic field. Both views are perfectly valid, and help one to picture what is happening.

Induced e.m.f. due to a Changing Magnetic Field in a Stationary Circuit

The coil, connected to the centre-zero galvanometer (as in the previous experiment), is placed near a similar coil which is in series with a 1·5 V cell and a tapping key (fig 3.4). When the key is depressed, a momentary current suddenly begins to flow in the primary coil. The magnetic flux lines associated with the current-carrying coil suddenly spread out threading the secondary coil, in which a momentary e.m.f. is set up and a current detected. By winding the coils on a soft iron core, the magnitude of the e.m.f. in the secondary coil is considerably increased.

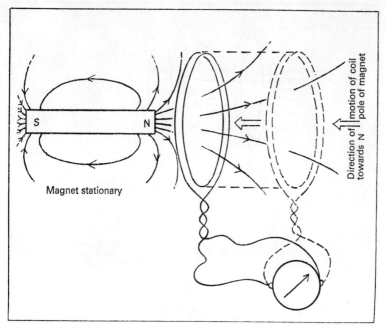

Fig 3.3 *An 'induced' e.m.f. is obtained when magnetic flux lines are 'threaded' or 'cut'*

So far the direction of the induced e.m.f. has been noted but not specified. Lenz and Faraday both discovered how to determine this direction, Lenz expressing his results in a form which has come to be known as *Lenz's law*: 'The direction of the induced e.m.f. or current is such that it opposes the change producing it.' The law follows from the principle of the conservation of energy.

Refer again to fig 3.2. Suppose that when the N pole of the magnet approaches the coil, the current in the coil flows in such a direction as to make the face of the coil nearest the approaching magnet act like a S pole. The N pole of the magnet would then be attracted, causing it to move faster, thus inducing a larger current and a stronger S polarity. Thus, in this system where mechanical energy is converted to electrical energy, the mechanical energy of the magnet and the electrical energy in the coil would both increase, which clearly contradicts the conservation of energy. The supposition must have been wrong and in fact, the direction of the current induced in the coil is such as to make the end of the coil facing the approaching

63

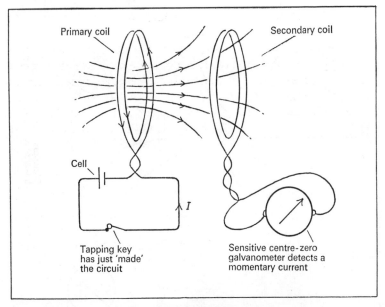

Fig 3.4 *A momentary current flows in the secondary when the primary circuit is 'made' or 'broken'. The primary flux threads the secondary. (The secondary flux is not shown)*

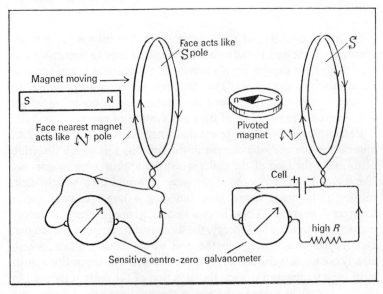

Fig 3.5 *Verification of Lenz's law*

N pole also act like a N pole. This induced pole clearly opposes the change which is producing the current.

An experiment confirms this conclusion. Suppose the N pole moving towards the coil produces a galvanometer deflection to the right. A battery with a suitable high resistance is inserted into the circuit to give a similar deflection to the right (see fig 3.5). The face of the coil is now tested using a pivoted compass needle and is indeed found to be a N pole. (The sensitivity of the galvanometer may have to be reduced so that a larger current can be used to deflect the compass needle.)

Faraday's Law of Electromagnetic Induction

A straight conductor being moved at right angles through a magnetic field is a good example of a conductor 'cutting' across lines of magnetic flux and having induced in it a momentary seat of e.m.f. Suitable apparatus (fig 3.6) consists of a length of conductor con-

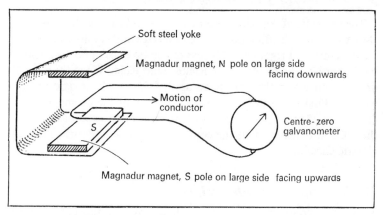

Fig 3.6 *An induced current flows in the circuit when the straight conductor cuts across magnetic flux*

nected by flexible leads to a sensitive centre-zero galvanometer. When the conductor is moved at right angles (for maximum effect) to a magnetic field provided, say, by two magnadur magnets which have their poles on the large flat sides, a deflection is noted on the galvanometer. The direction of the induced e.m.f. is reversed if the motion of the conductor is reversed; and it is also observed that the magnitude of the induced e.m.f. depends on the speed with which the conductor cuts across the lines of flux.

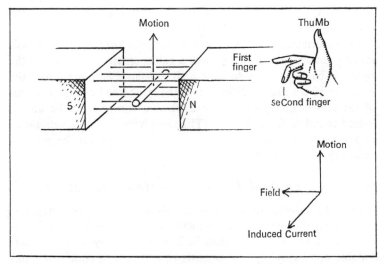

Fig 3.7   *Fleming's Right-Hand Rule*

The necessity of applying both Lenz's law and Fleming's Left-Hand Rule to predict the direction of the induced e.m.f. in a straight conductor cutting at right angles across magnetic lines of flux is avoided by the application of Fleming's Right-Hand Rule: 'If the thumb and first two fingers of the right hand are held mutually at right angles, with the First finger pointing in the direction of the magnetic Field, and the thuMb in the direction of Motion of the conductor, then the seCond finger predicts the conventional direction of the induced electric Current.'

Deduction of Faraday's Law

Suppose a conductor is pulled with a force F_1 through a short distance δs in time δt at right angles to a uniform magnetic field of flux density B (see fig 3.8). Then the work done $= F_1 \, \delta s$. If the induced e.m.f. E moves a charge Q, then the electrical energy obtained from the mechanical work done $= E \, Q$.

$$\therefore \quad E \, Q = F_1 \, \delta s$$

$$\therefore \quad E = \frac{F_1 \, \delta s}{Q}.$$

This induced e.m.f. opposes the motion which is producing the

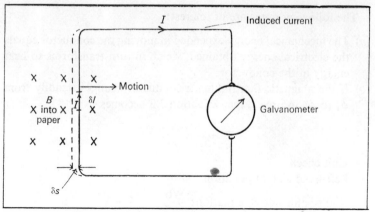

Fig 3.8 *Deduction of Faraday's law $E = -N\dfrac{d\phi}{dt}$*

e.m.f., and this opposition shows itself as a mechanical force F_2 in opposition to the force F_1 such that $F_2 = -F_1$.

But $$F_2 = B\,Q\,v_d \qquad \text{(equation 2.3)}$$

$$\therefore \quad F_2 = B\,Q\,\frac{\delta l}{\delta t},$$

where δl is the short distance through which the charge Q has drifted in time δt.

Therefore $$E = -\frac{F_2\,\delta s}{Q} = -\frac{B\,Q}{Q}\,\frac{\delta l \times \delta s}{\delta t} = -\frac{B\,\delta A}{\delta t}$$

where $\delta A = \delta l \times \delta s$ is the area of flux cut.

In the limit as $\delta t \to 0$,

the induced e.m.f. $$E = -\frac{B\,dA}{dt} = -\frac{d\phi}{dt}.$$

If N conductors are considered instead of 1 conductor, the total magnetic flux cut $= N\,d\phi$

$$E = -N\frac{d\phi}{dt}. \qquad (3.3)$$

This is *Faraday's law*, which states in words that the induced e.m.f. in a conductor is directly proportional to the rate at which the magnetic flux linking the conductor is changing. The negative sign is a consequence of the law of conservation of energy.

The following notes are of interest:

(a) The mechanical energy expended in moving the conductor equals the electrical energy obtained, which in turn transforms to heat energy in the conductor.

(b) If the magnetic flux linking a conductor changes steadily from ϕ_1 to ϕ_2 in time t, then equation 3.3 becomes

$$E = -N \frac{\phi_2 - \phi_1}{t}.$$

Unit check:

Left-hand side of equation: V

Right-hand side of equation: $\dfrac{\text{Wb}}{\text{s}} = \dfrac{\text{V s}}{\text{s}} = \text{V}$

(c) In the case of the conductor, length l, moving with constant velocity v at right angles to a magnetic flux density B, the flux cut per second $\dfrac{\mathrm{d}\phi}{\mathrm{d}t} = B\dfrac{\mathrm{d}A}{\mathrm{d}t} = B\,l\,v$

induced e.m.f. $E = -B\,l\,v.$ (3.4)

In the general case of the conductor moving at angle θ to the direction of the magnetic field, $E = -B\,l\,v\sin\theta.$

Magnitude of Induced Electric Charge

Suppose that the magnetic flux linking a coil of N turns changes from ϕ_1 to ϕ_2. If the coil is in a circuit of total resistance R, and the rate of flux change through the coil is $\dfrac{\mathrm{d}\phi}{\mathrm{d}t}$, then

instantaneous induced e.m.f. $E = -N\,\mathrm{d}\phi/\mathrm{d}t$
instantaneous induced current $I = E/R$

But $I = \dfrac{\mathrm{d}Q}{\mathrm{d}t}$ (the rate of flow of electric charge)

$$\therefore \qquad \frac{\mathrm{d}Q}{\mathrm{d}t} = -\frac{N}{R}\frac{\mathrm{d}\phi}{\mathrm{d}t}$$

$$\therefore \qquad \int_0^Q \mathrm{d}Q = -\frac{N}{R}\int_{\phi_1}^{\phi_2} \mathrm{d}\phi$$

hence $\qquad\qquad Q = -\dfrac{N(\phi_2 - \phi_1)}{R}.$ (3.5)

Thus, the quantity of electric charge, which is induced to move, is directly proportional to the change in flux linkage, and inversely proportional to the resistance of the circuit containing the coil, but it is independent of the time taken for the flux change to occur. The negative sign in front of the expression on the right-hand side of the equation (equation 3.5) only indicates that the charge is induced to drift in such a direction as to oppose the change of flux causing the charge to drift.

Worked Example

Calculate the number of electrons which are caused to drift in the metal frame of a window, which is in the side of a building parallel to the magnetic meridian and which is opened through 90°. (Assume: area of window $A = 0.8$ m^2; horizontal component of earth's magnetic field $B_x = 1.8 \times 10^{-5}$ tesla; resistance of metal frame $R = 10^{-2}$ Ω; charge on electron $e = 1.6 \times 10^{-19}$ C.)

Let N be the number of electrons caused to drift. Change in area of flux linked when window opens $A = 0.8$ m^2

$$\therefore \quad \text{flux change} \quad = B_x A = 1.8 \times 10^{-5} \times 0.8 \text{ Wb}$$

$$\therefore \quad \text{induced charge} \quad Q = \frac{\text{flux change}}{\text{resistance}} = \frac{1.8 \times 10^{-5} \times 0.8}{10^{-2}}$$

$$= 1.44 \times 10^{-3} \text{ C.}$$

But $\quad Q = N e \quad$ (equation 1.1)

$$\therefore \quad \text{number of electrons caused to drift} = \frac{1.44 \times 10^{-3}}{1.6 \times 10^{-19}} = 9 \times 10^{15}.$$

Use of Ballistic Galvanometer to measure Magnetic Flux Density

The quantity of charge induced in a coil is directly proportional to the change in magnetic flux linking the coil (see equation 3.5). Thus, if a coil, usually called a search coil, is connected to an instrument which measures the induced charge, then this also gives a measure of the change in magnetic flux or magnetic flux density through the search coil. Such an instrument is a *ballistic galvanometer*, which is a moving-coil galvanometer with two special features:

(*a*) The periodic time of oscillation of the moving part is made large, e.g. 2 seconds. This ensures that the induced charge, which must be momentary, passes through the coil *before* the coil has had time to leave its zero position. This short burst of current is said to 'fling' the coil. More advanced theory shows that the first throw θ is proportional to the charge Q which has flowed. A moving-coil galvanometer used in this way is said to be used ballistically. When it is used in conjunction with a search coil, $\theta \propto$ *flux change through the search coil.*

(*b*) The electromagnetic damping in a ballistic galvanometer is made small by winding the coil on a plastic frame. When the coil, and the frame on which it is wound, are flung from the zero position, they cut across the radial magnetic field of the galvanometer. E.m.f.s are induced, causing eddy currents in the coil (not in the plastic frame), which oppose the motion of the coil. The magnitude of the eddy current, and hence of the amount of damping, depends on the resistance of the galvanometer-search coil circuit. Provided this resistance is kept constant, the effect of the eddy current damping in the coil affects all throws equally and can be neglected.

A moving-coil galvanometer intended for measuring currents, takes up its final deflected position quickly because it has a short period of oscillation and because a metal frame for the coil causes such heavy damping, that the coil takes up its deflected position without oscillation. Such a galvanometer can still be used ballistically, though it does not give such reliable results.

The use of the 'ballistic galvanometer-search coil' technique is illustrated by the following two experiments:

Flux Cutting and Flux Threading

Both these terms were first used when a model was described which would explain the induced e.m.f. in a conductor passing through a magnetic field (see p. 61). Are these two terms equivalent and does Faraday's law apply in each case?

In fig 3.9, an alternating current of approx. 2 ampere is passed through the coil of an electromagnet and gradually reduced to zero so that there is no residual magnetic field between the pole pieces. A small search coil, connected to a ballistic galvanometer, is held between the pole pieces so that the plane of the coil is perpendicular to the magnetic field. First the search coil is withdrawn quickly from the pole pieces—no deflection on the galvanometer confirms that there is no residual field.

The search coil is replaced, and a direct current of, say, 2 ampere

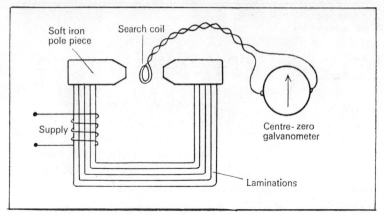

Fig 3.9 *Demonstration of magnetic flux 'threading' and magnetic flux 'cutting'*

is switched on in the coil of the electromagnet. The deflection θ is noted on the ballistic galvanometer. Magnetic flux ϕ has 'threaded' the search coil to produce this deflection. When the ballistic galvanometer coil has returned to its zero position, the search coil is withdrawn rapidly, this time 'cutting' the magnetic flux ϕ. The deflection on the ballistic galvanometer is found to be the same as before. This experiment confirms that flux cutting and flux threading are equivalent and that Faraday's law applies to both cases.

Experimental Investigation of the Flux Density B along the Axis of a Current-carrying Solenoid

A long solenoid (approx. 60 cm long and 6 cm in diameter) is connected in series with a variable low voltage d.c. supply, an ammeter and a key. A search coil, fixed to the end of a cardboard tube marked off in cm, can slide inside the solenoid and may be placed at any point on the axis either inside ($+$ve) or outside ($-$ve) the solenoid taking the end of the solenoid as the origin. The search coil is connected to a ballistic galvanometer (fig 3.10). With the search coil in the centre of the solenoid, the sensitivity of the galvanometer is adjusted until a reasonably large throw is obtained on switching the solenoid current off (say 1 ampere). Readings of the 'first throw' are recorded for a series of positions of the search coil, and the graph in fig 3.11 shows the points, marked by a cross, which were obtained in such an experiment. The throw of the ballistic

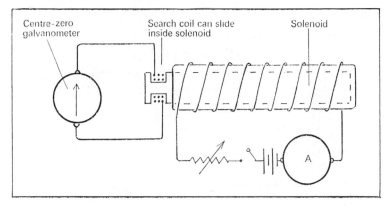

Fig 3.10 *Investigation of the flux density B along the axis of a current-carrying solenoid*

galvanometer is directly proportional to the mean flux density B in the plane of the search coil.

A comparison of the value of B at the end, and at the centre of the long solenoid, confirms the 'Biot–Savart equation deduction' (p. 53) that B at the end of a long solenoid has half the value of B at the centre.

The interpretation of the results may be extended to check equation 2.15. If θ_c is the first throw when the search coil is at the centre

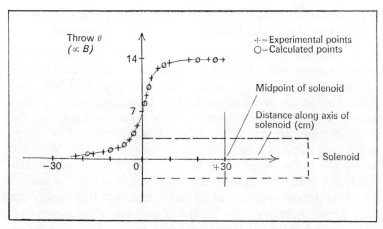

Fig 3.11 *Variation of the magnetic flux density B along the axis of a current-carrying solenoid*

of the solenoid, then the throw θ may be calculated for other positions of the search coil by rewriting equation 2.15 as follows:

$$\theta = \theta_c (\cos \alpha_1 - \cos \alpha_2).$$

Points calculated from this equation are shown as circles in fig 3.11. Agreement between experimental and theoretical values is very satisfactory.

Absolute Determination of the Ohm

As previously explained on p. 53, the absolute determination of an electrical unit is made in terms of μ_0 and the basic units, i.e. the metre, kilogramme and second.

A suitable apparatus for the absolute determination of the ohm is shown in fig 3.12. A metal disc rotates about an axis through its

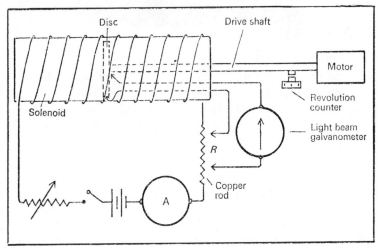

Fig 3.12 *Principle of the absolute determination of the ohm by the rotating disc method*

centre, the plane of the disc being perpendicular to the uniform magnetic flux density B at the middle of a long current-carrying solenoid of N/l turns per metre. The induced e.m.f. E between the axis and circumference of the disc is balanced against the potential drop along a section of the low resistance R, which also carries the current I flowing through the solenoid.

Induced e.m.f. $\quad E = -N\dfrac{\mathrm{d}\phi}{\mathrm{d}t} \qquad$ but $N = 1$

73

$$\therefore \qquad E = -B\frac{dA}{dt}$$

$$\therefore \qquad E = -BAf \qquad\qquad (3.6)$$

where A in metre^2 is the effective area of the disc (i.e. area of disc – area of axle) and f is the number of revolutions of the disc per second.

For balance:

$$IR = BAf = \mu_0\frac{N}{l}IAf$$

$$\therefore \qquad R = \mu_0\frac{N}{l}Af.$$

Unit check of the right-hand side of the equation:

$$\frac{\text{Vs}}{\text{Am}}\times\frac{1}{\text{m}}\times\frac{\text{m}^2}{1}\times\frac{1}{\text{s}} = \frac{\text{V}}{\text{A}} = \Omega.$$

A convenient method for the experiment is as follows:

(1) The disc is turned steadily by a motor, the number of revolutions per second being noted on the revolution counter. The very sensitive light beam galvanometer becomes deflected to a new position, indicating that a thermo-electric current is flowing. This is due to heating between the brass disc and the carbon brushes which make contact with the axle and the circumference of the disc.

(2) When this deflection θ is steady, the solenoid current (say 1 ampere) is switched on, and the movable contacts on the copper rod R are adjusted until the reading on the galvanometer is unchanged from θ. The current is then switched off and on, and if this has no effect on the galvanometer current (i.e. θ), then the potential drop between the movable contacts on R equals the induced e.m.f. E between the axis and circumference of the rotating disc.

(3) From the length and cross-sectional area of the copper rod used of resistance $R = \mu_0\,Af\,N/l$, the resistivity of copper is determined. A specification is then drawn up for a $1\,\Omega$ resistor of, say, 32 s.w.g. enamelled copper wire.

Mutual Induction

Simple experiments with primary and secondary coils which are close together (p. 62) show that a changing primary current induces an e.m.f. in the secondary, which opposes the change in the primary current. What quantitative relations exist between the various quantities involved?

Suppose a change in primary flux $\delta\phi_p$ is caused by a change in primary current δI_p in time δt. If all this change in flux threads the secondary coil of N_s turns, then the change in flux linkage is $N_s\,\delta\phi_p$. The instantaneous induced e.m.f. in the secondary, E_s (as $\delta t \to 0$) is given by Faraday's law:

i.e. $$E_s = -N_s\frac{d\phi_p}{dt}.$$

Now the change in flux linkage $N_s\,\delta\phi_p$ depends on, and is in fact directly proportional to δI_p (by Biot–Savart equation).

Therefore, as $\delta t \to 0$, $E_s \propto -\dfrac{dI_p}{dt}$.

This proportionality, written as an equation, becomes

$$E_s = -M\frac{dI_p}{dt}. \tag{3.7}$$

The constant of proportionality M is called the mutual inductance of the two circuits. The negative sign (from Lenz's law) makes M a positive quantity, because E_s is always in opposition to dI_p/dt, and hence of opposite sign.

The unit of M is $\dfrac{V\,s}{A} = V\,s\,A^{-1}$. This derived unit is called the henry (H).

The henry is defined from equation 3.7: 'A mutual inductance of 1 henry is possessed by two circuits if an e.m.f. of 1 volt is induced in the secondary when the primary current changes uniformly at the rate of 1 ampere per second.' In the above equations, $N_s\,d\phi_p = M\,dI_p$, and mutual inductance M may be defined as the magnetic flux linking the secondary when the primary current is 1 ampere.

Mutual Inductance of Two Air-cored Solenoids

Just as the resistance of a conductor may be calculated from the resistivity of the material and the dimensions of the conductor, so the mutual inductance of two circuits may be calculated from the permeability of the medium surrounding the circuits and the dimensions of the circuits.

Consider the case of a long solenoid (primary), of cross-sectional area A_p, with N_p/l_p turns per metre, in which a small change in current δI_p in time δt causes a change in magnetic flux $\delta\phi_p$. Suppose this change of flux links a coaxial coil (secondary) of N_s turns, which is at the middle of the solenoid and which can either just slide over the solenoid or which can just slide inside the solenoid of cross-sectional area A_p.

The instantaneous induced e.m.f. in the secondary is given by Faraday's law. As $\delta t \to 0$,

$$E_s = -N_s \frac{d\phi_p}{dt}$$

$$\therefore \quad E_s = -N_s A_p \frac{dB_p}{dt}$$

where B_p is the magnetic flux density at the middle of the long solenoid, given by $\quad B_p = \mu_0 \frac{N_p}{l_p} I_p \quad$ (see equation 2.16).

From substitution, $\quad E_s = -\left[N_s A_p \mu_0 \frac{N_p}{l_p} \right] \frac{dI_p}{dt}$.

Compare with equation 3.7,

$$M = \mu_0 N_s A_p \frac{N_p}{l_p}. \tag{3.8}$$

Unit check:

Right-hand side of the equation: $\dfrac{H}{m} \times 1 \times \dfrac{m^2}{1} \times \dfrac{1}{m} = H$ (henry).

Worked Example

The primary of a mutual inductor is a long air-cored solenoid 50 cm long, 5·0 cm in diameter and having 1000 turns. How many turns are required on the secondary solenoid if the mutual inductance is to be 4·0 mH? (Assume $\mu_0 = 4\pi \times 10^{-7}$ H m^{-1}.)

The mutual inductance of air-cored coaxial solenoids is given by equation 3.8:

$$M = \mu_0 N_s A_p \frac{N_p}{l_p}$$

$$\therefore \quad N_s = \frac{M \, l_p}{\mu_0 \, A_p \, N_p}.$$

Given: Mutual inductance $\quad M = 4 \, \text{mH} = 4 \times 10^{-3} \, \text{H}$

Primary turns per unit length $\dfrac{N_p}{l_p} = \dfrac{1000}{50 \times 10^{-2}} = 2 \times 10^3 \, \dfrac{\text{turns}}{\text{metre}}$

Primary cross-sectional area $\quad A_p = \pi \, r^2 = \pi \times (2 \cdot 5)^2 \times 10^{-4} \, \text{metre}^2$

$$= 6 \cdot 25 \pi \times 10^{-4} \, \text{metre}^2$$

$$N_s = \frac{4 \times 10^{-3}}{4 \pi \times 10^{-7} \times 6 \cdot 25 \pi \times 10^{-4} \times 2 \times 10^3}$$

$$= 808 \text{ turns}$$

i.e. 808 turns are required to be wound on to the secondary solenoid.

Calibration of Ballistic Galvanometer by Mutual Inductance

The sensitivity of a ballistic galvanometer is defined as the deflection per unit charge, θ/Q divisions per coulomb. A mutual inductor, of known mutual inductance, e.g. air-cored coaxial solenoids, can be

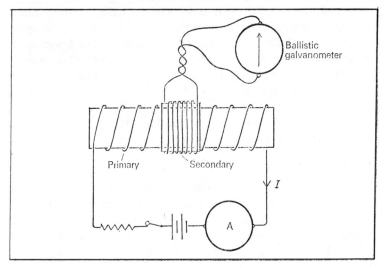

Fig 3.13 *Calibration of a ballistic galvanometer by a known mutual inductance*

used to calibrate the ballistic galvanometer. A variable low voltage d.c. supply is connected in series with the primary solenoid, an ammeter and a switch. The ballistic galvanometer is connected to the secondary (see fig 3.13). The first throw θ on the ballistic galvanometer is noted when a known primary current I_p (say 2A) is switched off.

If the total resistance of the secondary and the ballistic galvanometer is R, and the change in magnetic flux linking the secondary is $N_s \, \phi_p$, then the charge induced Q is given by equation 3.5

$$Q = -\frac{N_s \, \phi_p}{R}.$$

Now $\qquad E_s = -N_s \frac{d\phi_p}{dt} = -M \frac{dI_p}{dt}$ (from equation 3.7).

Therefore $N_s \, \phi_p = M I_p$ where a change of current I_p in the primary of a mutual inductance M causes a change in secondary flux linkage $N_s \, \phi_p$

$$\therefore \quad Q = -\frac{M I_p}{R}.$$

Q is calculated from this equation and hence θ/Q follows.

It should be noted that the deflection of a ballistic galvanometer depends on the resistance of the galvanometer circuit. The lower R, the greater is Q and hence the greater is eddy current damping. If the ballistic galvanometer is to be used with a search coil to measure magnetic flux density, then the search coil can be included in series with the galvanometer and secondary of the mutual inductor during calibration and this circuit can then be used for the measurement. The amount of damping is now constant during calibration and measurement and no corrections need be made.

Self Induction

A coil of wire carrying a current is threaded by its own magnetic flux. Whenever the current changes, there must then be a change in the magnetic flux linking the coil, and consequently an e.m.f. is induced *in the coil*, which opposes the change of current in the coil. The coil is said to possess self inductance, and this effect is most important in a.c. circuits.

Suppose a change in flux $\delta\phi$ is caused by a change in current δI in time δt. If the coil has N turns, the change in flux linkage is $N\,\delta\phi$. The instantaneous induced e.m.f. (as $\delta t \to 0$) is given by Faraday's law:

$$\text{i.e.} \qquad E = -N\frac{\mathrm{d}\phi}{\mathrm{d}t}.$$

But $N\,\mathrm{d}\phi \propto \mathrm{d}I$ (Biot–Savart equation)

$$\therefore \quad E \propto -\frac{\mathrm{d}I}{\mathrm{d}t}.$$

This proportionality, written as an equation, becomes

$$E = -L\frac{\mathrm{d}I}{\mathrm{d}t}. \qquad (3.9)$$

The constant of proportionality L is called the self inductance of the coil. The unit of L is the same as for mutual inductance M,

$$\text{i.e.} \qquad \frac{\mathrm{V\,s}}{\mathrm{A}} = \mathrm{H}\ (\text{henry}).$$

In the above equations, $N\,\mathrm{d}\phi = L\,\mathrm{d}I$, and self inductance L may be defined as the magnetic flux linkage when the current in the coil is 1 ampere.

Inductance of an Air-cored Solenoid

Consider a long solenoid with N/l turns per metre, in which a small change in current δI in time δt causes a change in magnetic flux $\delta\phi$. The instantaneous induced e.m.f. (as $\delta t \to 0$) is given by Faraday's law:

$$E = -N\frac{\mathrm{d}\phi}{\mathrm{d}t}$$

$$\therefore \quad E = -N A\frac{\mathrm{d}B}{\mathrm{d}t}$$

neglecting end effects, $\qquad B = \mu_0\,\dfrac{N}{l}\,I$

$$\therefore \quad E = -\left[N A \mu_0\,\frac{N}{l}\right]\frac{\mathrm{d}I}{\mathrm{d}t}$$

79

Compare with equation 3.9,

$$L = \frac{\mu_0 \, A \, N^2}{l}. \tag{3.10}$$

Worked Example

Calculate the inductance of a long air-cored solenoid 50 cm long, with 1000 turns and of mean diameter 5 cm. ($\mu_0 = 4\pi \times 10^{-7}$ H m^{-1}.)

The inductance of the solenoid is given by equation 3.10,

i.e. $\quad L = \dfrac{\mu_0 \, A \, N^2}{l}.$

Given: Cross-sectional area $\quad A = \pi \, r^2 = 6 \cdot 25\pi \times 10^{-4}$ m^2

number of turns $\quad\quad N = 10^3$ turns

length of solenoid $\quad\quad l = 5 \times 10^{-1}$ m

$$\therefore \; L = \frac{4\pi \times 10^{-7} \times 6 \cdot 25\pi \times 10^{-4} \times (10^3)^2}{5 \times 10^{-1}}.$$

$$\therefore \; L = 4 \cdot 9 \times 10^{-3} \text{ H}.$$

The inductance of the solenoid is 4·9 millihenry.

The Rotating Coil in a Uniform Magnetic Field

One of the most important practical applications of the basic principles of electromagnetic induction is the rotating coil generator or a.c. dynamo.

Consider a plane coil of N turns and cross-sectional area A to be rotating uniformly with angular velocity ω in radians second^{-1} (i.e. f revolutions second^{-1}, where $\omega = 2\pi f$), with the axis of rotation at right angles to a uniform magnetic flux density B. When the plane of the coil is perpendicular to the field, the magnetic flux linkage is a maximum; however, the *rate of change* of magnetic flux linkage is zero and so there is no induced e.m.f. in the coil. Taking this position as the starting point, consider the plane of the coil to have turned through angle θ in time t (see fig 3.14).

Now $\theta = \omega t$, and the area perpendicular to B is $A \cos \omega t$. Therefore the magnetic flux linkage $N \phi = N B A \cos \omega t$.

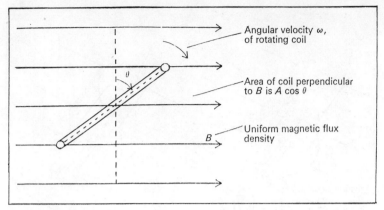

Angular velocity ω, of rotating coil

Area of coil perpendicular to B is $A \cos \theta$

Uniform magnetic flux density

B

θ

Fig 3.14 *The instantaneous value of the induced e.m.f. in the coil is given by $E = E_{max} \sin wt$*

By Faraday's law,

instantaneous induced e.m.f. $\qquad E = -N \dfrac{\mathrm{d}}{\mathrm{d}t}(B\,A\cos\omega t)$

$$= -B\,A\,N\dfrac{\mathrm{d}}{\mathrm{d}t}(\cos\omega t)$$

$$= -B\,A\,N\,(-\sin\omega t \times \omega)$$

$$\therefore \quad E = B\,A\,N\,\omega\sin\omega t.$$

When $\theta = \omega t = 90°$, $\sin\omega t = 1$

$$\therefore \quad E_{\text{max}} = B\,A\,N\,\omega$$

and $\qquad\qquad\qquad\qquad E = E_{\text{max}}\sin 2\pi ft.$ \hfill (3.11)

The a.c. and d.c. Dynamo

It is seen from equation 3.11, that the magnitude of the instantaneous induced e.m.f. E (and the resulting induced current) is directly proportional to the flux density B, the cross-sectional area A and number of turns of the coil N, and the speed of the rotation of the coil. The magnitude of E also follows a sine wave variation.

How can the induced currents be 'delivered' to an external circuit? The two ways are illustrated in fig 3.15. In an a.c. dynamo, the current flows through carbon brushes which touch two *slip rings*, each ring being in electrical contact with one end of the coil which

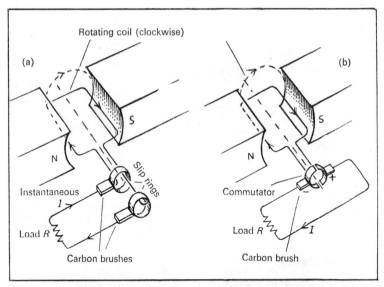

Fig 3.15   (*a*) *Principle of a simple a.c. dynamo*
           (*b*) *Principle of a simple d.c. dynamo*

can rotate between the poles of a magnet. In the d.c. dynamo, the two halves of a *split-ring commutator* replace the slip rings, and the brushes are so arranged that when the coil is passing through the vertical position, the brushes change contact from one half of the split ring to the other. The wave forms of the current from a single-

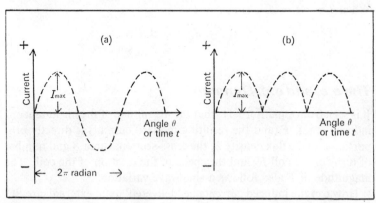

Fig 3.16   *The waveform of the current in an external load R (see fig 3.15)*
           (*a*) *from a single coil a.c. dynamo*
           (*b*) *from a single coil d.c. dynamo*

coil dynamo are then similar to the graphs in fig 3.16. It is seen that the action of the split-ring commutator is to give unidirectional current in an external circuit.

In practical dynamos, a number of coils are wound in slots cut in a laminated soft iron cylinder called an armature, the coils having equal angular separation. Considering such a d.c. dynamo, each coil has its own pair of segments in a multi-segment commutator, and the current from such a dynamo is fairly steady with only a slight ripple.

When the induced current flows in the rotating coil which is cutting across magnetic flux, the coil will tend to behave like a motor. An application of Fleming's rules indicates that the forces act to oppose the rotation of the coil. Thus the mechanical work done, say, by a turbine in turning the coil is the work done in overcoming the forces of the 'reverse motor effect', and that amount of energy is then associated with the induced current in the form of energy dissipated in the coil as heat and available electrical energy in the external circuit.

The d.c. Motor

The above discussion on the 'reverse motor effect' illustrates the fact that a d.c. dynamo can be used as a d.c. motor if a battery is connected to the brushes touching the split-ring commutator. Referring to fig 3.15(b), by Fleming's Left-Hand Rule, forces act to rotate the coil. This rotation is made continuous by reversing the direction of the current each time the coil is vertical. This can be seen in fig 3.15. The motion is made less jerky in a practical motor by using several coils wound in slots cut in a laminated soft iron armature, the coils having equal angular separation and being connected to a multi-segment commutator.

When the rotating coil cuts across the magnetic flux, an e.m.f. is induced in the coil which will tend to oppose the rotation of the coil. This 'back e.m.f. E_b' has to be subtracted from the applied e.m.f. E of the battery to obtain the net e.m.f. driving a current I through the coil of resistance R.

Therefore $$(E - E_b) = I R$$

and $$E I t = I^2 R t + E_b I t$$

i.e. the electrical energy expended in time t by the battery equals the energy dissipated in the coil as heat and the work done in rotating the coil, which is really the work required to overcome the induced back e.m.f. It should be noted that when the armature is stationary, the back e.m.f. is zero, and the coil current is given by $I = E/R$. To avoid a dangerously large initial current when a practical d.c. motor is started, a resistance is connected in series with the motor. This resistance is then reduced as the speed of the motor increases. When a steadily turning motor is suddenly required to cope with some additional mechanical work, the motor slows, thus reducing the back e.m.f. because magnetic flux lines are not being cut as rapidly. The current in the coil increases, i.e. the current drawn from the battery or other supply increases, and extra electrical energy is expended to do the additional mechanical work.

Questions

(Take $g = 9\cdot81 \text{ m s}^{-2} = 9\cdot81 \text{ N kg}^{-1}$.)

1. State the laws of electromagnetic induction.

Describe an experiment you would perform to illustrate the law governing the direction of the induced e.m.f.

State the formula for the e.m.f. induced in a straight wire moving in a magnetic field and show clearly the relative directions of the field, the motion and the induced e.m.f.

A rectangular coil of wire is mounted with its axis perpendicular to a magnetic field and rotated at a constant speed of f revolutions per second. Calculate the magnitude and direction of the induced e.m.f. in the various parts of the coil when its plane is instantaneously at an angle θ to the magnetic field. Hence calculate the resultant e.m.f. in the coil at that instant.

A copper tube of length 30 cm pointing east–west is dropped with its axis parallel to the ground from a height of 10 metres. Calculate the e.m.f. produced in it at the moment it strikes the ground. The horizontal component of the earth's magnetic field is $1\cdot8 \times 10^{-5}$ tesla. (S.C.E.)

2. Write down the formula for the force acting on a straight current-carrying conductor at right angles to a uniform magnetic field and say what each symbol stands for.

Use this formula to derive an expression for the e.m.f. developed across the ends of the conductor when it is moved at a velocity v so as to cut the flux normally.

Lenz's law has parallels in other branches of physics—quote any *one* example you can think of.

A copper rod 1 m long lies east–west and is supported at its ends by two vertical copper guide rails. The rod is allowed to fall freely from rest through a distance of 10 m and the p.d. across the guide rails at the end of the fall is found to be 0·28 mV. Calculate the horizontal flux density due to the earth's magnetic field.

The same rod is now moved on horizontal guide rails at a steady velocity of 10 m s^{-1} to produce a p.d. of 0·4 mV. Calculate the vertical flux density of the earth's magnetic field.

Now use your two results to find the angle of dip at that locus.

(S.C.E.)

3. Obtain an expression for the potential difference across the ends of a wire moving through a magnetic field B with a velocity v where the wire, its direction of motion and B are all at right angles to one another.

How would you modify the expression for the general case when B is not perpendicular to v?

A straight wire of length 2 metres moves with a velocity of 10 m s^{-1} in a direction at right angles to a uniform magnetic field. When a very low resistance meter is connected across the ends of the wire a current of 4μA flows. If the resistance of the wire is 100 Ω, find the magnitude of the magnetic flux density B. If, in the above situation, the wire was twice as long and twice the diameter what current would then flow in the wire?

(B.Ed. Edinburgh)

4. A simple pendulum swings in a plane which is at right angles to a uniform magnetic field of flux density B and consists of a light conducting wire of length l to which is attached a bob that may be considered to be a point mass m. A small needle attached to the underside of the bob dips into a pool of mercury. Find an expression for the maximum potential difference between the upper end of the wire and the mercury when the maximum angular displacement of the bob is θ. If a current I is passed through the suspension find an expression for the final static angular displacement of the pendulum. Assume that the wire remains straight. (J.M.B. Special)

5. Show that the quantity of electricity moved in a circuit by a change of magnetic flux is independent of the time taken for the change to occur.

A 50-turn search coil of cross-sectional area 1 cm^2 is situated with its plane at right angles to a magnetic field of flux density 0·1 tesla. Calculate the charge induced to flow in the search coil circuit of total resistance 25 ohm when the coil is withdrawn from the magnetic field.

6. How is the design of a sensitive moving-coil galvanometer modified to make it suitable for ballistic use?

Referring to any one experiment you have performed or seen performed, explain in detail how a search coil and ballistic galvanometer may be used to measure changes in magnetic flux.

7. A solenoid 0·6 m long, uniformly wound with 1200 turns of wire, carries a current of 0·5 A. A short coil of 400 turns of mean diameter 0·06 m, is placed inside the solenoid, in the uniform part of the field, with its plane at right angles to the flux. This secondary coil is connected in series with a coil of 20 turns of mean area of cross-section 2×10^{-4} m^2, and a ballistic galvanometer. The 20-turn coil is placed between the poles of a powerful permanent horseshoe magnet. Reversal of the current of 0·5 A in the solenoid gives a ballistic deflection of 24·0 divisions. The maximum deflection which can be obtained on rapid removal of the small coil from between the poles of the magnet is 20·0 divisions. Calculate the flux density in the gap of the magnet. Explain your calculation. (Take $\mu_0 = 4\pi \times 10^{-7}$ H m^{-1}.)   (O. & C. part)

8. A copper disc of effective area A has its axle coincident with the axis of a long air-cored solenoid of N/l turns per metre carrying a steady current I. The plane of the disc is perpendicular to the magnetic flux density B, and the disc is rotated steadily at f revolutions per second. The resultant induced e.m.f. E between the rim and the axle of the disc is balanced against the p.d. between the ends of a low resistance R, which carries the same current as the solenoid.

Write down expressions for
(a) the induced e.m.f. E
(b) the p.d. across R.
Deduce an equation which enables R to be calculated.

In a particular experiment, the effective radius of the disc $= 2.5$ cm, $N/l = 2 \times 10^3$ turns per metre and $f = 6$ revolutions per second. Assuming the permeability for air $= \mu_0 = 4\pi \times 10^{-7}$ H m^{-1}, calculate a value for R.

9. A copper disc of effective radius 10 cm rotates 20 times per second with its plane perpendicular to a uniform magnetic field. If the induced e.m.f. between the centre and edge is 3·14 millivolt, what is the magnetic flux density of the field?

10. Describe an absolute method of measuring resistance, explaining clearly how the resistance in ohms may be calculated from experimentally measured quantities. Suggest reasonable values for the dimensions and other experimental parameters which would be suitable for measuring a resistance of 0·01 ohm.

Why is the method not suitable for the measurement of large resistances, and how can the values of large resistances be obtained in absolute ohms? ($\mu_0 = 4\pi \times 10^{-7}$ henry m^{-1})   (O. & C. Special)

11. Define self inductance and mutual inductance.

Explain the differences in structure and action between a ballistic and an aperiodic galvanometer.

A ballistic galvanometer of resistance 15·0 ohms and sensitivity 5·0 divisions per micro-coulomb is connected in series with a resistance of 100 ohms and a secondary coil of 500 turns and of resistance 50 ohms. This coil is wound round the middle of a long solenoid of radius 3·0 cm having 10 turns cm^{-1} and carrying a current of 0·60 A. Assuming no damping, calculate the deflexion produced in the galvanometer when the current in the solenoid is switched off. ($\mu_0 = 4\pi \times 10^{-7}$ H m^{-1}.)   (L.)

12. Explain the special features that are necessary in a moving-coil galvanometer intended for ballistic use.

A ballistic galvanometer is connected in series with a search coil and the secondary winding of a mutual inductance. When a current is reversed in the primary winding of the inductance a charge of 90 microcoulombs flows through the galvanometer. After switching off the primary current the search coil (which has 200 turns of mean diameter 1·00 cm) is pla· d in and perpendicular to a magnetic field. The deflection of the galvanometer caused by the rapid removal of the search coil from the magnetic field is the same as was observed when the primary current was reversed. The total resistance of the

87

galvanometer circuit is 250 ohms. Calculate the magnetic flux density of the magnetic field. Draw a complete circuit diagram of the arrangement. (J.M.B.)

13. Explain how the mutual inductance of a pair of air-cored solenoids may be calculated from the dimensions and the number of turns on the mutual inductor.

Design a mutual inductor (two air-cored solenoids) to have a mutual inductance of approximately 1 mH, the primary having a maximum length of 30 cm and a maximum diameter of 3 cm. (Take the permeability for air $= \mu_0 = 4\pi \times 10^{-7}$ H m^{-1}.)

14. Describe in detail the calibration of a ballistic galvanometer using a mutual inductance.

15. Explain what is meant by self inductance and define the practical unit in which it is measured.

Describe and explain an experiment which demonstrates the phenomenon of self-induction. (J.M.B.)

16. State the laws of electromagnetic induction.

Describe the construction and action of a device of practical importance which makes use of the principle of electromagnetic induction.

A closed circular loop of wire of radius 5 cm is placed with its plane at right angles to a uniform magnetic field in which the flux density is changing at the rate of 0·01 tesla per second. Calculate (a) the e.m.f. induced in the loop, (b) the energy dissipated in the loop in 10 seconds if its resistance is 2 ohms. (The self inductance of the loop may be ignored.)

Explain why there is a tension in the loop while the magnetic field is changing. How does it vary with time? (O. & C.)

17. Calculate the maximum induced e.m.f. in a plane coil of 40 turns and cross-sectional area 10 cm^2 which is rotated about an axis perpendicular to a magnetic flux density of 0·6 tesla at 5 revolutions per second.

18. State the laws relating to (a) the direction, (b) the magnitude of an induced e.m.f. Describe the structure and mode of action of a simple form of a.c. generator, pointing out how the laws stated are applied in the design of the machine.

How may the generator be modified to yield direct current? (L.)

19. State what is meant by 'back-e.m.f.' with reference to an electric motor.

Why is there a risk of burning out the armature windings of an electric motor when the normal voltage is applied but the armature is prevented from rotating? (S.C.E. part)

20. State Lenz's law in electromagnetic induction and describe an experiment to verify it. Imagine a case in which the law is not obeyed and describe the consequences.

Calculate the peak e.m.f. which is generated when a plane coil of wire of 20 turns and area $2 \cdot 0$ cm^2 is rotated at 100 revolutions per minute, the axis of the coil being at right angles to a field of magnetic flux density $0 \cdot 5$ T. (A.E.B.)

Chapter 4

Magnetic Properties of Matter

Magnetism

What is Magnetism? Why is magnetism exhibited so strongly in just a few substances, such as iron, nickel and cobalt? Are all elements magnetic? If magnetism is a property of all matter, how can it be explained in terms of atoms and groups of atoms? What theories and what models enable one to explain, for example, the directional property of a freely suspended piece of magnetite, used as a compass over two thousand years ago by Chinese travellers? What is the difference between an unmagnetised bar of iron or steel and the same bar when it is magnetised? What different properties of manganese and bismuth cause manganese (like iron) to be attracted towards the stronger part of a non-uniform magnetic field and bismuth to be repelled towards the weaker part of a non-uniform magnetic field? These are a few of the questions, based on experimental evidence, to which theories of magnetism using suitable models have to try to find possible answers.

The difference in behaviour of substances when they are subjected to the influence of a non-uniform magnetic field forms the basis of a three-fold classification of materials. It is found that all substances, including liquids and gases, fall into one of three types shown in Table 4.1.

An electromagnet with pole pieces similar to those shown in fig 4.1, has non-uniform regions of magnetic flux density as illustrated by the spacing of the magnetic flux lines. Such an electromagnet, provided it is strong enough (magnetic flux density of the order of 0·1 T), may be used to distinguish between ferro-, para-, and diamagnetic substances. A very strong magnetic field is obtained for a few seconds at a time by passing a large direct current (say 6 A) through the magnetising coils. Decide on the maximum permissible

Table 4.1. Classification of magnetic materials.

Type	Action on substance in a non-uniform magnetic field	Example
ferromagnetic	strongly attracted into the stronger part of the field	short cylindrical sample of iron
paramagnetic	weakly attracted into the stronger part of the field	concentrated solution of manganous sulphate
diamagnetic	weakly repelled from the stronger part of the field	short cylindrical sample of bismuth

value of the direct current, then pass an alternating current through the coils and gradually reduce to zero so that there is no residual magnetic field between the pole pieces. A short cylindrical sample of iron is suspended freely near the pole pieces. When the magnetic field is switched on briefly, the iron is attracted very strongly and it

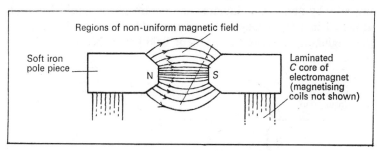

Fig 4.1 *Non-uniform magnetic field suitable for distinguishing between ferro-, para- and diamagnetic materials*

moves rapidly into the strongest part of the magnetic field, the axis of the cylinder lining up with the direction of the magnetic field. This effect is characteristic of the *ferromagnetic* materials, which include iron, steel, nickel and cobalt, and alloys such as Alnico, Alcomax, Ticonal and Magnadur.

The attraction of a *paramagnetic* substance into the stronger part of a non-uniform magnetic field is illustrated with a concentrated solution of manganous sulphate, contained in a U-tube. Once any residual magnetic field is removed, by gradually reducing an alter-

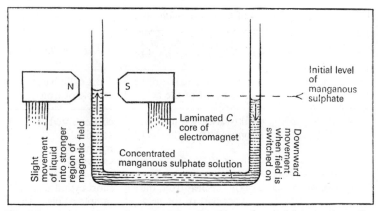

Fig 4.2 *A paramagnetic material moves into the stronger region of a non-uniform magnetic field*

nating current in the coils of the electromagnet, one meniscus is arranged to be in the lower half between the polepieces (fig 4.2). When the strong magnetic field is switched on briefly, the manganous sulphate solution in the weaker part of the non-uniform field moves upwards by about a millimetre—the paramagnetic liquid has been attracted into the stronger part of the field. The liquid returns to the original levels when the magnetic field is switched off.

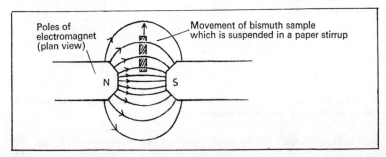

Fig 4.3 *A diamagnetic material moves away from the stronger region of a non-uniform magnetic field*

The *diamagnetic* effect is demonstrated with a short, cylindrical sample of bismuth, which is suspended in a light paper stirrup between the demagnetised polepieces in the position shown in fig 4.3. When the strong magnetic field is switched on briefly, the bismuth sample moves about a millimetre in a direction away from the stronger part of the magnetic field, showing that a diamagnetic substance is repelled from the stronger parts of a non-uniform field. Again the sample returns to its original position when the magnetic field is switched off.

Amperian Currents

Although para- and diamagnetic effects were not classified until 1845 by Faraday, the idea of explaining the known phenomena of ferromagnetism in the early part of the nineteenth century in terms of electric currents was proposed by Ampère soon after Oersted's discovery of the magnetic effect of an electric current. Realising that an electric current flowing in a coil acted like a small magnet (magnetic dipole), Ampère made the rather speculative suggestion that magnetic properties were the resultant effect of a large number of tiny current loops within the material. These small current loops, requiring no e.m.f. to keep the electric charge flowing, were postulated to be randomly orientated in the unmagnetised state. The process of magnetisation consisted of the aligning of the current loops under the influence of an external magnetic field, so that the magnetic field of each current loop reinforced the external magnetic field.

Some of the present-day experimental evidence for the postulate that the source of magnetism is electric charge in motion has already been examined in chapter 2, e.g. the equivalence of the magnetic field patterns of a current-carrying solenoid and a permanent bar magnet of the same dimensions is illustrated in fig 2.4, and the similarity of the action of an applied magnetic field on a freely suspended

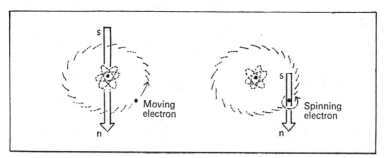

Fig 4.4 *The moving planetary and spinning electrons contribute to the magnetic field of an atom*

current-carrying solenoid and bar magnet is illustrated in figs 2.17 and 2.18.

Ampère's model of current loops is now accepted, the current loop being interpreted in terms of moving planetary and spinning electrons in the atom, rather as in fig 4.4. Thus magnetism is a property of all matter.

The simplest practical analogy to an Amperian current loop is a flat coil of one turn carrying a steady electric current (see p. 36 and figs 2.15 and 2.16). If the axis of the current loop of area A carrying a current I makes angle θ with the uniformly applied magnetic flux density B, then the torque T trying to align the magnetic field due to the current loop with the external field is given by equation 2.5.

$$\text{i.e.} \qquad T = B\,I\,A \sin \theta$$

$$\text{or} \qquad T = B\,m \sin \theta$$

where the product $I\,A = m$ is defined as the electromagnetic moment of the current loop. The electromagnetic moment may be thought of as the property of the current loop that decides the torque (moment of a couple) which will act on the current loop when flux density B acts at angle θ to the axis of the loop.

As explained on p. 39, electromagnetic moment is a vector quantity, and its positive direction is the same as the positive direction of the axial magnetic flux density due to the current loop.

Paramagnetism and Diamagnetism

Fig 4.5 shows a plan view of a rectangular current loop carrying a current I in the direction shown. The electromagnetic moment vector is aligned with the uniform external magnetic field of flux density B and the forces F (in newtons) acting on the vertical sides of length a are given by $F = B\,I\,a$. The two forces are equal and opposite.

Suppose now that the above current loop is in a non-uniform magnetic field, the stronger part of the field being represented by a closer spacing of the magnetic flux lines (see fig 4.6). The force F_{strong} on the vertical side carrying the current out of the plane of the paper and situated in the stronger part of the magnetic field of magnetic flux density B_{strong} is given by

$$F_{strong} = B_{strong}\,I\,a.$$

Similarly $F_{\text{weak}} = B_{\text{weak}} I a$

the net force experienced by the loop is given by

$$F_{\text{net}} = F_{\text{strong}} - F_{\text{weak}}$$
$$= (B_{\text{strong}} - B_{\text{weak}}) I a,$$

and the direction of the force on the current loop is into the stronger part of the non-uniform magnetic field.

Hence a model for ferro- and paramagnetic materials, which move into the stronger part of a non-uniform magnetic field (p. 91), requires the assumption that the particles of the material contain current loops with a resultant electromagnetic moment. Such current loops tend first of all to align themselves with the direction of the external magnetic field (subject to thermal agitations), and then a force $F = \sum F_{\text{net}}$ acts on the specimen, where $\sum F_{\text{net}}$ is the sum of all the net forces on individual current loops.

A model for diamagnetic materials requires that the particles of the material have a zero resultant electromagnetic moment. The effect of the external magnetic field on the current loops is one of electromagnetic induction, the direction of the 'induced current' being such that the induced magnetic field is in a direction opposing the external field. Such a model is illustrated in fig 4.7, and as may be seen from the diagram, the net force on such a particle is away from the stronger part of a non-uniform magnetic field. When the external magnetic field is switched off, the induced effects disappear also.

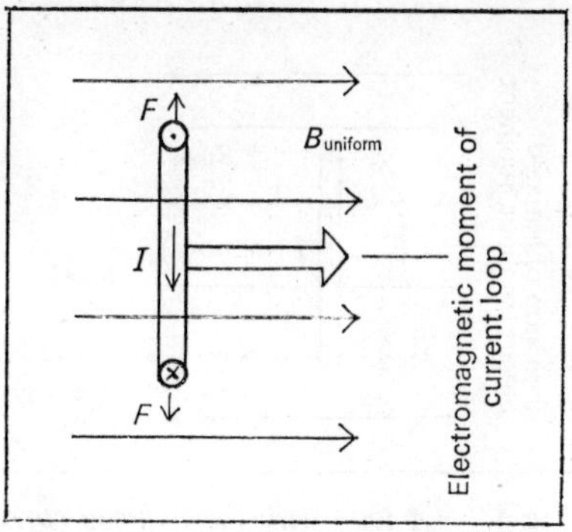

Fig 4.5 Plan view of a current loop, with its electromagnetic moment vector aligned with the direction of the uniform applied magnetic field. Net force on vertical sides is zero

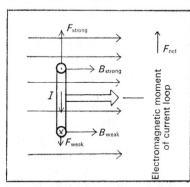

Fig 4.6 The current loop experiences a net force into the stronger region of the applied non-uniform magnetic field

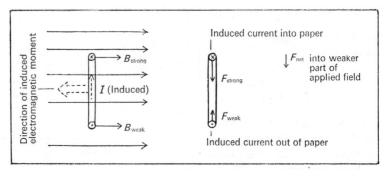

Fig 4.7 *A loop with the induced current as shown experiences a net force into the weaker region of the applied non-uniform magnetic field*

It follows from the above discussion that all materials are affected by the 'diamagnetic effect', which is independent of temperature since no alignment is required. If particles have a resultant magnetic moment, however, then the paramagnetic effect masks the diamagnetic effect, and since more violent thermal agitation tends to impede alignment of the current loops, paramagnetic effects decrease as the temperature increases.

Ferromagnetism and the Domain Theory

One of the questions posed at the beginning of this chapter still requires an answer—why is magnetism exhibited so strongly by iron, nickel and cobalt? What special mechanism allows such a high degree of alignment of Amperian current loops in these materials in spite of the usual thermal agitation of the atoms?

In 1928, Heisenberg used concepts of quantum physics in proposing a hypothesis, later confirmed, that it is the particular distribution of electrons in the two outer electron orbits of ferromagnetic elements which gives rise to two strong forces, whose origin cannot be 'explained' in terms of classical physics (see p. 6). One of the forces holds the atoms firmly together; the other force holds the electromagnetic moment vectors of neighbouring atoms parallel. There is then in ferromagnetic materials a natural tendency for neighbouring atoms to align their electromagnetic moment vectors, even in the *absence* of an external magnetic field, and they do so in groups of about 10^{14} atoms. Such a group of atoms is called a 'domain', and there are normally thousands of such domains in a small crystal of the material. Each domain is magnetically 'saturated' with all the aligned Amperian current loops contributing to a resultant electromagnetic moment for the domain. Thus each domain acts rather like a tiny permanent magnet which has a very large magnetic flux density associated with it.

The existence of magnetic domains in a ferromagnetic crystal was demonstrated by Bitter in 1931. He deposited very finely divided

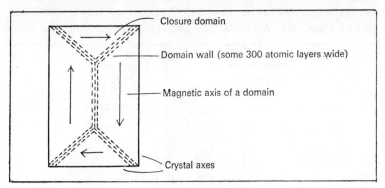

Fig 4.8 *Domains in an unmagnetised ferromagnetic crystal form closed loops. There is a little magnetic flux leakage at domain walls*

ferromagnetic particles in a colloidal suspension on the polished surface of a ferromagnetic crystal. The particles gather at the edges of the domains where there is some leakage of magnetic flux and a 'Bitter pattern', illustrated in fig 4.8, is observed through a microscope. The unmagnetised crystal does not exhibit external magnetic properties because the domains form a series of closed magnetic loops. The closure domains act rather like keepers on a pair of bar magnets—they eliminate what are called self-demagnetising effects.

The domains are separated by a domain wall of finite width, in which the electromagnetic moments of neighbouring atoms successively make small angles with each other until the change in direction of the electromagnetic moment vector from one domain to its neighbour has been achieved.

During the magnetisation process, those domains having their magnetic axes in the general direction of the externally applied field grow by domain wall movement which can be observed with special techniques. The size of the other domains in the material diminish so that more and more electromagnetic moment vectors line up with the external field. When all the domain axes are aligned with the direction of the external field, then the material is fully magnetised, i.e. saturated.

The Curie Temperature

Can domains continue to exist as the temperature of the ferromagnetic material is raised? Fig 4.9 shows a piece of JAE metal, which is a ferromagnetic alloy (70% Ni, 30% Cu), attracted to a magnet which is suspended in a beaker of water at room temperature. At a temperature of about 343 K, called the Curie temperature for JAE metal, the JAE metal falls away from the magnet. The JAE

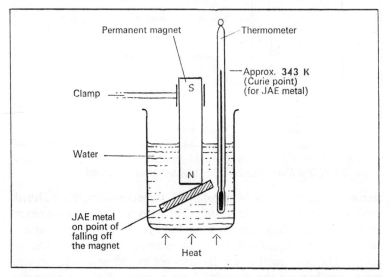

Fig 4.9 *When the Curie temperature is reached and exceeded, a ferromagnetic material becomes paramagnetic*

metal becomes strongly magnetic again if the temperature is lowered below the Curie temperature. The conclusion is that when the Curie temperature is reached and exceeded, the thermal vibrations become so violent that the domain structure breaks down, and the ferromagnetic becomes a paramagnetic material. For iron, nickel and cobalt the Curie temperatures are 1043 K, 631 K and 1388 K respectively.

The Magnetic Field of a Solenoid and Toroid

An experimental investigation of the variation of the magnetic flux density B_0 along the axis of an air-cored current-carrying solenoid using the search coil/ballistic galvanometer method was described on p. 71. The results confirmed the deduction made from the 'Biot–Savart equation', that the magnetic flux density falls off from the middle of the solenoid to half the 'middle value' at the end of the solenoid (see fig 3.11). It follows that if a solenoid is to be used to try to magnetise a ferromagnetic rod uniformly, then the solenoid must be very long compared with the rod. There is, moreover, the serious difficulty of the self-demagnetisation effect near the ends of the rod, which makes it impossible to achieve uniform magnetisation in a rod-shaped specimen. Both objections are overcome if the ferromagnetic material is in the form of a closed magnetic loop, i.e. ring-shaped, with a toroidal coil (toroid) wound all the way round the 'anchor ring'. In such an arrangement (fig 4.10), the magnetising field is uniform all *along* the ring, and there is

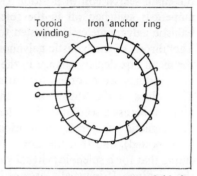

Fig 4.10 *The magnetising field due to the current-carrying toroid is uniform all along the iron anchor ring*

no self-demagnetisation. The value of the magnetic flux density B_0 within an air-cored toroid of N/l turns per metre carrying a current I is given by more advanced theory to be

$$B_0 = \mu_0 \frac{N}{l} I,$$ where μ_0 is the permeability of free

space $= 4\pi \times 10^{-7} \text{ H m}^{-1}$.

This is the same as equation 2.16, applicable to the middle region of a long solenoid.

Is the magnetic flux density B_0 uniform *across* a section of a toroid, to give uniform magnetisation of the ring specimen? Is B_0 contained inside the winding? An experiment using a solenoid and

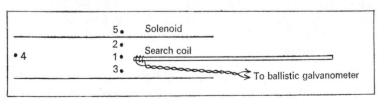

Fig 4.11 *Exploration of the magnetic field pattern of a solenoid*

a small diameter (say 2 cm) search coil connected to a ballistic galvanometer provides important evidence (fig 4.11). A long solenoid (approx. 60 cm long and 6 cm in diameter) is connected in series with a variable low voltage d.c. supply, an ammeter and a key. With the small search coil in position 1, a magnetising current of say 1 ampere is switched off in the solenoid and the sensitivity of the ballistic galvanometer is adjusted to give a reasonably large throw. The 'throw' of the ballistic galvanometer is directly proportional to the mean flux density change in the plane of the search coil (p. 70), and readings are recorded for various positions of the search coil. The values of the 'throw' show that the magnetic flux density is uniform across a section of the solenoid in positions 1, 2 and 3, that the magnetic flux density in position 4 is half the value in position 1 (as expected), and that the throw in position 5 is very small, indicating that for a solenoid, virtually all the magnetising field is inside the winding. It is usually assumed that the conclusions regarding both the uniformity of the magnetic flux density across a section of the solenoid and the fact that nearly all B_0 is contained inside the winding are also applicable, to a first approximation to a toroid, provided that the diameter of the toroid winding is quite small compared with the diameter of the toroid itself. This assumption can be tested by using a section of flexible spring (e.g. 'slinky') in the shape of an arc of a toroid. If the factor N/l for the toroid is less than for the solenoid, a larger current, say 4 A, is required to be switched off in the toroid winding to give a suitable throw on the ballistic galvanometer.

Magnetic Polarisation and Relative Permeability

Suppose the magnetic flux density due to the magnetising current in a toroid is B_0. If the toroid is completely filled with a ferromagnetic material such as iron, then the above magnetising field will cause domain wall movement (p. 97). Depending on the strength of B_0, the number of atoms with their own magnetic flux density vector in the direction of B_0 increases. Let the ferromagnetic core provide additional flux density J, to produce a total flux density B within the toroid.

Then $$B = B_0 + J \quad \text{(in teslas)}. \qquad (4.1)$$

The quantity $J = B - B_0$ is called the magnetic polarisation in the ring-shaped specimen — it is a measure of the degree of alignment of the atoms with the direction of the applied magnetising field B_0. Complete alignment produces magnetic saturation and J then has its maximum value.

When comparing magnetic materials, it is useful to know the ratio of the total magnetic flux density B in a ferromagnetic toroid compared with the applied magnetic flux density B_0. This ratio is called the relative permeability μ_r of the ferromagnetic material, and is defined by equation 4.2.

$$\mu_r = \frac{B}{B_0} \qquad (4.2)$$

Notes

(a) As B and B_0 are measured in the same units i.e. tesla, it follows that μ_r has no units.

(b) Equation 4.2 holds if the magnetic flux density within the material is uniform, a condition which is satisfied in a ring-shaped specimen. If a gap is made in the ring, self-demagnetising effects must be taken into account, and equation 4.2 then requires modification.

The Magnetisation Curve

How does the total magnetic flux density B within a toroid completely filled with a ferromagnetic ring (say iron) increase with the applied magnetic flux density B_0?

Fig 4.12 shows a labelled circuit diagram of the apparatus suitable for determining the relation between B and B_0 for an iron ring. The graph of B against B_0 or more simply a graph of measurable quantities proportional to B and B_0 respectively, is called the magnetisation curve for the specimen.

In the diagram, a variable low voltage d.c. supply is connected *via* the reversing switch to the toroid having N/l turns per metre. If the magnetising current is I, then the magnetic flux density B_0 is given by $B_0 = \mu_0 I N/l$ (p. 99). B_0 is directly proportional to the magnetising current I. The total flux density B in the iron toroid is determined by the search coil/ballistic galvanometer method (p. 69). When the magnetising current I giving a certain value of B_0 is reversed, the throw θ of the ballistic galvanometer is directly proportional to the change in flux density through the 12-turn search coil. Here the throw θ is proportional to *twice B*, since the current has been *reversed*. A graph of $\theta/2$ (proportional to B)

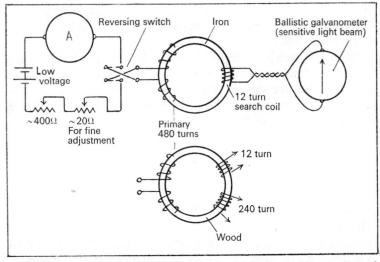

Fig 4.12 *Determination of relation between B and B_0 for iron and wood ring-shaped specimens*

against I (proportional to B_0) will give the correct shape of the magnetisation curve.

To find the most suitable sensitivity for the ballistic galvanometer, the magnetising current I is set at its maximum value of approximately 3 A (to achieve saturation), and it is reversed at least 20 times to put the iron into a 'cyclic condition'. (If this reversing procedure is omitted, unreliable results are obtained for B.) The ballistic galvanometer isolating switch is now closed and the magnetising current is reversed. By adjusting a series resistance in the galvanometer circuit, a suitably large throw is obtained.

With the isolating switch open again, the iron ring is demagnetised by repeatedly reversing the current through the toroid while it is being slowly reduced from the maximum of 3 A to zero. Here the reversal of direct current being reduced to zero is equivalent to an alternating current being gradually reduced to zero.

The magnetising current is now increased from zero to (say) 25 mA, and the iron is put into a cyclic condition. The ballistic galvanometer throw on reversing the current is recorded. This procedure is repeated in 25 mA steps initially, later larger incremental steps of 0·1 A and 0·2 A suffice up to 3 A.

The experiment is repeated with a non-ferromagnetic wood toroid (fig. 4.12) of the same dimensions as the iron toroid. This time the

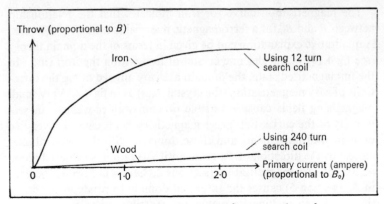

Fig 4.13 *Magnetisation curves for iron and wood*

magnetisation and cycling procedures are not necessary. Using the same sensitivity setting for the ballistic galvanometer as in the iron experiment, useful readings of θ can only be obtained using the 240-turn search coil. A sample of throws for current settings at $\frac{1}{2}$ A intervals indicates direct proportion between magnetising current I and the throw $\theta/2$.

The values of $\theta/2$ ($\propto B$) are plotted against I ($\propto B_0$), and the graphs for the iron and wood toroids are shown in fig 4.13.

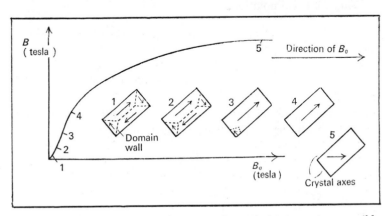

Fig 4.14 *Domain theory explanation of magnetisation. 1—reversible domain wall movement; 2, 3, 4—irreversible domain wall movement; 5—domain rotation into direction of applied field*

The magnetisation curve for iron indicates that the relationship between B and B_0 for a ferromagnetic material is extremely complex. A qualitative explanation can be given in terms of the domain theory (see fig 4.14). Consider one crystal of iron within the iron ring. In the unmagnetised state, the domain axes are aligned along the directions of easy magnetisation (the crystal axes) as in fig 4.8. Very small magnetising fields cause reversible domain wall movement in section (1) of the curve, but larger magnetising fields cause irreversible domain wall movements and those domains with their crystal axes closest to the direction of B_0 grow until saturation is achieved along an axis of easy magnetisation (sections 2, 3 and 4). Further increase in B_0 (section 5) causes the saturated domain to rotate in the direction of B_0, so making its maximum contribution to the magnetic polarisation J, where $J = B - B_0$ (equation 4.1). A graph of J against B_0 would level off parallel to the B_0 axis, since complete alignment of all domain axes has been achieved with the direction of the magnetising field.

Variation of Relative Permeability with Applied Flux Density

It is clear from the graph in fig 4.13 that the relative permeability for iron, $(\mu_r)_{\text{iron}} = B/B_0$, is not a constant, but has a value which depends on B_0. The variation of μ_r with B_0 may be determined from the magnetisation curves for iron and wood as follows:

Using the usual notation,

$$B = \mu \frac{N}{l} I \qquad \text{in the iron toroid}$$

$$B_0 = \mu_0 \frac{N}{l} I \qquad \text{in the 'free space' toroid}$$

where μ and μ_0 are the permeabilities of iron and free space respectively. Substituting for B and B_0 in equation 4.2,

$$\mu_r = \frac{B}{B_0} = \frac{\mu}{\mu_0}$$

or $\qquad\qquad \mu = \mu_r\mu_0.$ \hfill (4.3)

The total magnetic flux density in the iron and wood toroids has been increased by the cores from:

$$B_0 = \mu_0 \frac{N}{l} I \quad \text{to} \quad B_{\text{iron}} = (\mu_r)_{\text{iron}} \mu_0 \frac{N}{l} I \quad \text{and}$$

$$B_{\text{wood}} = (\mu_r)_{\text{wood}} \mu_0 \frac{N}{l} I \quad \text{respectively.}$$

Now the charge Q, induced in a search coil of N_s turns and mean area A, when the magnetic flux density through the coil changes by $2 \times B$, is given by equation 3.5

i.e.
$$Q = -\frac{N_s A \times 2B}{R}$$

where R is the resistance of the search coil circuit. Since the resistance of the 12-turn (or even 240-turn) search coil is still very small compared with the resistance of the ballistic galvanometer, R may be taken as constant in both the experiments. The negative sign indicates that the charge is induced to drift in such a direction as to oppose the change of flux density.

Now the throw θ of the ballistic galvanometer is proportional to Q

i.e. $\theta = k Q$, where k is a constant.

$$\theta = k \times -\frac{N_s A}{R} \times 2\mu_r \mu_0 \frac{N}{l} I.$$

The search coils had 12 and 240 turns for the iron and wood toroids respectively:

$$\frac{\theta_{\text{iron}}}{\theta_{\text{wood}}} = \frac{k \times -\dfrac{12A}{R} \times 2 (\mu_r)_{\text{iron}} \mu_0 \dfrac{N}{l} I}{k \times -\dfrac{240A}{R} \times 2 (\mu_r)_{\text{wood}} \mu_0 \dfrac{N}{l} I}.$$

A wood core, inserted into an air-cored solenoid, used as the primary of a mutual inductor (p. 74), has no measurable effect on the total magnetic flux density within the solenoid, so to a good approximation $(\mu_r)_{\text{wood}} = 1$. Substituting for $(\mu_r)_{\text{wood}}$ and cancelling the above equation becomes:

$$(\mu_r)_{\text{iron}} = \frac{240}{12} \times \frac{\theta_{\text{iron}}}{\theta_{\text{wood}}}.$$

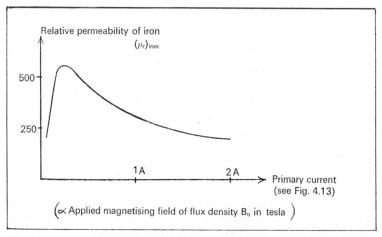

Fig 4.15 *Variation of the relative permeability of iron with applied flux density B_0*

The values of $(\mu_r)_{iron}$ are now worked out for all the values of current I used in the iron experiment, as illustrated in table 4.2.

Table 4.2. Deduction of the variation of the relative permeability of iron with applied magnetic flux density.

Magnetising current I (ampere)	θ_{iron} (cm of deflection)	θ_{wood} (cm of deflection)	$\dfrac{\theta_{iron}}{\theta_{wood}}$	$(\mu_r)_{iron}$
0·025 0·050 0·075 . . .	exptl. results . . .	from the straight line magnetisation graph for wood	for each value of I . .	for each value of I . .

The variation of $(\mu_r)_{iron}$ with applied magnetising field is shown graphically in fig 4.15.

It should be noted that the value of the permeability μ of a medium depends on μ_r and on the magnitude and units of μ_0. In SI units, $\mu_0 = 4\pi \times 10^{-7}$ H m^{-1}, $\mu = \mu_r \times 4\pi \times 10^{-7}$ H m^{-1}.

Hysteresis Loops and Magnetic Materials

How does technology use different ferromagnetic materials? What makes a reliable permanent magnet? What are the desirable pro-

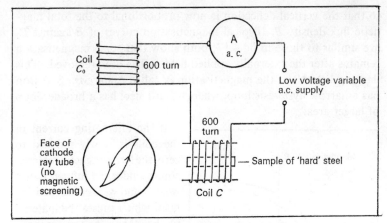

Fig 4.16 *Qualitative investigation of the effect of alternating magnetic fields on ferromagnetic materials*

perties of magnetic materials which are subjected to alternating magnetic fields as, for example, in generators, electromagnets and transformers?

A qualitative investigation of the effect of an alternating magnetic field on samples of 'soft' iron and 'hard' steel may be carried out with a demonstration oscilloscope having no magnetic screening. Two 600-turn coils are connected in series with a low voltage a.c. supply (fig 4.16) and the alternating current is set to approximately 1 A. The positions of the two coils are adjusted until a straight line at 45° to the horizontal is obtained on the screen. This is a B_0 versus B_0 graph, since coil C_0 produces horizontal deflections (Fleming's L.H.R.) proportional to B_0, and similarly coil C produces vertical deflections of the electron beam. Samples of 'soft' iron and 'hard' steel are introduced into coil C in turn

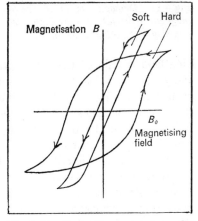

Fig 4.17 *Typical hysteresis loops for 'soft' ferromagnetic materials (e.g. soft iron and silicon steel), and 'hard' ferromagnetic materials (e.g. Alnico, permanent magnet steel)*

so that the vertical deflection is now proportional to the total magnetic flux density B. Typical magnetisation curves of B against B_0 are similar to those in fig 4.17; both show that some magnetisation remains after the externally applied field B_0 has been removed. This 'lagging behind' of the magnetisation is called *hysteresis*. Soft iron has a narrow hysteresis loop, whereas hard steel has a broader loop of larger area.

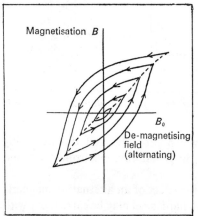

Fig 4.18   *Demagnetisation of a ferromagnetic material by a gradually decreasing alternating magnetic field*

If the alternating current in the coils is slowly reduced to zero, the ferromagnetic material comes under the influence of a weaker and weaker magnetising field, which causes the material to be taken round progressively smaller hysteresis loops (fig 4.18) until there is no magnetisation left.

The hysteresis effect is explained by the domain theory in terms of the irreversible domain wall movements (p. 104) past small 'obstacles', such as imperfections and non-magnetic inclusions, at crystal boundaries. When the magnetising field is reduced from its maximum saturation value to zero, many domain walls are trapped and cannot move back across the obstacles (causing the lagging behind, or hysteresis effect) until a reverse external magnetic field above some threshold value is applied. It is clear that the particular magnetic state of a ferromagnetic material depends on its immediate past magnetic history, and the 'cycling procedure' described on p. 102 gets the soft iron toroid into a particular hysteresis cycle.

Materials are called magnetically 'soft' if they are easy to magnetise and to demagnetise, or magnetically 'hard' if the opposite is the case. It follows, therefore, that permanent magnets (say for moving-coil galvanometers), must be made of hard materials which not only have a high degree of magnetisation, but which also retain their magnetism in spite of slight mechanical shocks or through the effect of stray magnetic fields.

On the other hand, materials used as cores in generators or transformers must be 'soft'. Silicon steels (about 3% Si), have a narrow hysteresis loop indicating easy magnetisation (high initial permeability), and easy demagnetisation in each cycle. The energy used up in traversing the loop, called the hysteresis loss, is therefore small. To obtain a high overall efficiency, it is also necessary to reduce to a minimum, heat losses due to induced eddy currents in the core. This is partly achieved by building the core out of laminations of silicon steel coated with an insulating layer. The electrical resistivity of steel can be increased further, and eddy current heating reduced, by the addition of a higher percentage (4·5%) of silicon; however, the silicon-steel then becomes more brittle. Such a material can be tolerated in a transformer core, but not in the rotor of a generator (or motor), where mechanical strength is very important.

Questions

1. Derive an equation for the torque T acting on a freely suspended flat coil of cross-sectional area A carrying a current I, when the axis of the coil makes angle θ with the applied uniform magnetic flux density B.

Use the equation to define clearly what is meant by the 'electromagnetic moment' of a current loop.

2. Compare the action of an externally applied magnetic field on a freely suspended flat current-carrying coil if the applied magnetic flux density is (a) uniform (b) non-uniform. Use clearly labelled diagrams to explain your answer.

3. Compare and contrast the magnetic properties of ferromagnetic, paramagnetic and diamagnetic substances, and give a qualitative account of the processes which occur in each of these three classes of magnetic material when subjected to an external magnetic field.

(L. Special)

4. Write a note on the role of magnetic domains in ferromagnetism.

(B.Ed. Edinburgh part)

5. What is meant by 'The Curie Temperature'?

Describe a simple experiment to measure the Curie Temperature for a ferromagnetic alloy.

Using the models of Amperian current loops and of domains, indicate the changes that take place in a ferromagnetic material as the Curie temperature is reached and exceeded.

6. Describe with full experimental detail how you would attempt to obtain a normal magnetisation curve for a specimen of iron, showing clearly how the calculations would be carried out, and sketching the form of curve expected.

A primary coil of 500 turns is wound uniformly on an iron ring of mean radius 10 cm and cross-sectional area 4 cm^2. A secondary coil of 50 turns is wound over the primary and connected to a ballistic galvanometer, the total resistance of the secondary circuit being 500 ohms. When a current of 2 A is reversed in the primary, the galvanometer indicates a throw of 10 divisions. When a capacitor of capacity 2 microfarads is charged to a potential difference of 20 volts and discharged through the same galvanometer, the throw obtained is 5 divisions. Calculate the magnetic permeability of the iron. (S.)

7. How does the domain theory of ferromagnetism explain the magnetisation curve for iron?

8. Define what you understand by
   (a) magnetic polarisation,
   (b) relative permeability.

By means of a sketch graph, indicate how the relative permeability of iron varies with the applied magnetic flux density.

9. An 'anchor ring' made of a ferromagnetic material is wound with a toroid of 200 turns, the inner radius being 4·5 cm and the outer radius 5·5 cm. A current of 1 ampere flows in the toroid.

Calculate:
   (a) the magnetic flux density B_0 along the axis of the air-cored toroid;
   (b) the total magnetic flux density B in the anchor ring, if the relative permeability of the ferromagnetic material is 500 for the applied value of B_0;
   (c) the magnetic polarisation for the applied value of B_0.

(Take the permeability of air = $\mu_0 = 4\pi \times 10^{-7}$ H m^{-1}.)

10. What information does a hysteresis loop provide about the suitability of different types of ferromagnetic material for a practical purpose? In particular, refer to the choice of material for
  (*a*) a permanent magnet,
  (*b*) the core of an electromagnet.   (L. part)

Chapter 5

The Electric Field and Electric Potential

Electrostatic Induction

Basic principles, such as the simple 'free electron' theory for metals and the 'law of conservation of electric charge', both of which were introduced in chapter 1, will now be used to explain the phenomenon of electrostatic induction, illustrated by the following experiment:

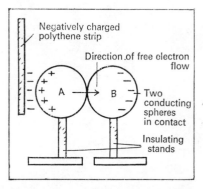

Fig 5.1 *The 'inducing' charge on the polythene strip causes charge separation in the conductor made up of two spheres A and B*

Two uncharged, insulated, conducting spheres A and B are placed in contact, and while a negatively charged polythene strip is held close to A (see fig 5.1), the spheres are separated. The charged strip is then removed. Spheres A and B are now brought in turn near the cap of a charged electroscope. Sphere A causes increased divergence in a positively charged electroscope, indicating that A has an induced positive charge. Similarly, sphere B causes increased divergence in a negatively charged electroscope, indicating that B has an induced negative charge. Further, if A and B are brought into contact again, they each lose their induced charges and become electrically neutral.

Using the free electron theory for metals, the above observations are explained by assuming that the negative inducing charge on the polythene strip repels free electrons (also negative) to the far end of the conductor made up of spheres A and B. When the spheres are separated, B is left with an induced excess of electrons and A with an equal deficiency of electrons; B is negatively charged and A is positively charged. Bringing the charged spheres into contact again (in the absence of the inducing charge) allows the electrons to distribute themselves equally and the spheres become electrically neutral. Such a separation of electric charges in a conductor, brought about by an 'inducing' charge which makes no contact with the conductor, is called electrostatic induction.

Faraday investigated electrostatic induction using his now famous 'ice-pail'. To repeat the experiments, a deep metal can is placed on the cap of an electroscope, and a negatively (say) charged sphere is lowered into the can without touching the inside. The leaf diverges, indicating an induced charge on the outside of the can and on the

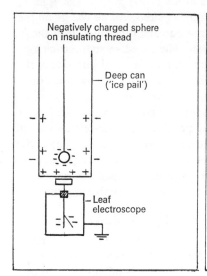

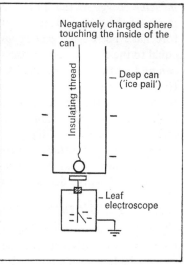

Fig 5.2 *The 'inducing' charge on the sphere causes charge separation between the inner and outer surfaces of the deep metal can conductor*

Fig 5.3 *The negative inducing charge on the sphere and the induced positive charge on the inside of the can have neutralised each other*

electroscope in contact with the outside of the can. The sign of the induced charge is found by touching the outside of the can with a proof plane, which is a small metal disc fixed to an insulating handle. The proof plane acquires a little of the charge under test. The charge on the outside is found to be negative (see fig 5.2), and the charge on the inside of the can, positive. When the charged sphere is removed from the can, the leaf collapses, showing that the *induced negative charge* on the outside of the can *equals* the *induced positive charge* on the inside of the can.

The similarity so far between the 'ice-pail' experiment and the 'two spheres' experiment will be clear to the student. However, Faraday was able to extend his 'ice-pail' experiment to find out whether there is a simple relation between the magnitudes of the *induced* and *inducing* charges. A negatively charged sphere is again lowered deep into the can, and the leaf diverges as before. When the sphere is made to touch the inside of the can (see fig 5.3), there is no change in the tilt of the leaf which still remains the same when the sphere is removed from the can. On testing, it is found that there is now no charge on the sphere or on the inside of the can, i.e. the *negative inducing charge* on the sphere and the *induced positive charge* on the inside of the can must have neutralised each other and must therefore have been *equal and opposite*. The negative induced charge, equal to the charge 'lost' by the sphere, remains on the outside of the can and on the electroscope. A third conclusion can then be drawn from the 'ice-pail' experiment; that any *excess charge on a conductor* is repelled to the limits of the conductor and *resides on the outside surface*. An investigation with a proof plane transferring charge from different areas of the can to an electroscope, shows that the charge density (electric charge per unit area of surface) is greatest where the surface has the greatest curvature i.e. near the rim of the can, and the charge density is least at places of small curvature.

Action at Points; the Van-de-Graaff Generator

The sharp point of a pin has very great curvature, and if the pin is charged sufficiently, the surface density of charge can become extremely high at such a point. Ions in the air of similar charge to that on the point are then strongly repelled. Such fast moving ions collide with air molecules causing further ionisation, and very quickly an 'avalanche' of ions moves rapidly away from the point, carrying air molecules along in an 'electric wind'. Ions of opposite charge to that on the pin point are attracted towards the point and neutralise the charge there. The net result is that the point apparently 'sprays off' its charge, and the student should understand what is meant by this figure of speech.

A sharp point can also 'collect' or 'draw off' charge. If a negatively charged polythene strip is held near the point of a pin Sello-

taped to the cap of an electroscope (see fig 5.4), then the leaf
diverges and remains tilted when
the strip is removed. A test
shows that the electroscope has
become negatively charged. The
explanation in terms of free
electron theory and the law of
conservation of charge is as
follows: The negative charge on
the polythene strip repels electrons and induces a positive
charge on the pin point and a
negative charge on the leaf of
the electroscope. Point action
then 'sprays' a positive ion wind

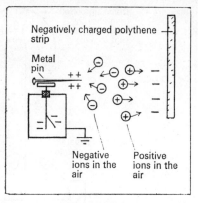

Fig 5.4   *A sharp pin point apparently
'draws off' charge from the charged
insulating strip*

on to the polythene strip, neutralising negative charge there, and
negative ions are attracted towards the point, neutralising the induced positive charge there. Hence the electroscope has gained
negative charge, while the polythene strip has lost some. The point
has apparently 'drawn off' electric charge, and the student should
again understand what is meant by this figure of speech.

The above effects are used in the Van-de-Graaff generator to build
up an electric charge on a hollow, spherically-shaped dome. Com-
mercial generators build up charge to a potential of millions of volts
to accelerate charged particles in atomic and nuclear investigations.
A simple school generator is shown in fig 5.5. Initially frictional
charge is developed between the motor-driven Perspex roller and the
rubber belt, and a negative charge is induced on the comb of metal
points P. P is earthed *via* the metal base and negative charge is
drawn from earth on to the points during induction. This negative
charge is then 'sprayed off' points P on to the moving belt and is
carried upwards until the comb of metal points Q is reached. Q is
connected to the inner surface of the dome. Here a positive charge
is induced on Q by the repulsion of negative charge on to the outer
surface of the dome. Negative charge has apparently been 'drawn
off' the moving belt on to the dome. Positive charge is 'sprayed off'
Q on to the downward moving belt. This cycle of operations is
continuous and the net result is a transfer of negative charge from
earth to the dome, the energy being provided by the motor in the

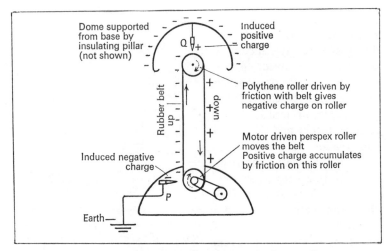

Dome supported from base by insulating pillar (not shown)

Induced positive charge

Q

Polythene roller driven by friction with belt gives negative charge on roller

Rubber belt

up

down

Motor driven perspex roller moves the belt
Positive charge accumulates by friction on this roller

Induced negative charge

P

Earth

Fig 5.5   *A simple school adaptation of the Van-de-Graaff generator*

form of work done against the repulsive force between the charged dome and the charged upward moving belt.

If a pin is Sellotaped at right angles to the dome, with its point facing away from it, then the 'electric wind' previously mentioned can be felt with the palm of the hand held nearby (not too near!). The ion wind may be strong enough to blow out a lighted taper.

Coulomb's Law of Force

A qualitative study of electric forces (chapter 1) led to the conclusion that like charges repel and unlike charges attract, What factors determine the magnitude of the force between electric charges? This question was asked at the end of the eighteenth century by a number of scientists, and the French physicist Charles Coulomb investigated the problem experimentally in 1785.

Coulomb used two small spherical pithballs C and D with gold surfaces. One of the spheres was fixed on an insulating stand and the other was attached to one end of a light horizontal insulating arm suspended from a fine silver wire (see fig 5.6). A third pithball E acted as a counterweight at the other end of this 'torsion balance'. The two spheres C and D were given like, equal charges and the force of repulsion was calculated from the angle of twist in the suspension wire for various distances between the charged spheres. Coulomb established within an accuracy of about 3% that the force

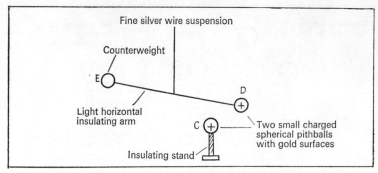

Fig 5.6 *Principle of Coulomb's torsion balance (in draught-free enclosure)*

F is inversely proportional to the square of the distance r between the centres of the charged spheres,

i.e. $$F \propto \frac{1}{r^2}.$$

It should be noted that in general the charges on spheres C and D are not evenly distributed because of the greater than average repulsion between charges (nearer than average) on surfaces facing each other. Therefore the distance apart of the centre of gravity of the charges is not the same as the distance r between the centres of the two spheres. In electrostatic theory a simplification is introduced by considering all the charge on a sphere to be concentrated at a point. The point charge—like the point mass in Newtonian mechanics—is a very useful theoretical concept; however, it should be understood that in practical terms point charges are only 'approached' when two small spheres are a large distance apart.

By the method of charge-sharing, illustrated in fig 5.7, Coulomb changed the charge on the spheres from Q to $\frac{1}{2}Q$ (and to $\frac{1}{4}Q$ etc.). Measuring the force of repulsion at a fixed distance r apart for various submultiples of charge, Coulomb concluded that the force F is proportional to the product of the two charges Q_1 and Q_2

i.e. $$F \propto Q_1 Q_2.$$

If these two experimental results are combined

$$F \propto \frac{Q_1 Q_2}{r^2}. \tag{5.1}$$

Equation 5.1 summarises Coulomb's Law.

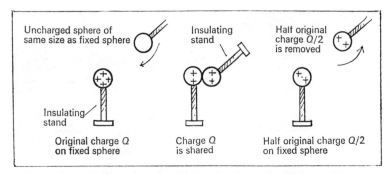

Fig 5.7 *The principle of 'charge-sharing'*

A simple technique for measuring the force between two charged metallised polystyrene spheres A and B, which does not require the use of a torsion balance, leads to Coulomb's Law fairly quickly. The apparatus is shown in fig 5.8. Sphere A is suspended at the bottom of a 'V' of fine nylon insulating thread, so that it can only swing in one vertical plane, which is perpendicular to the plane of

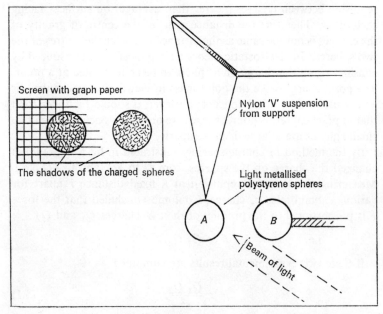

Fig 5.8 *Apparatus for a quantitative investigation of Coulomb's Law of Force*

suspension. Sphere B is glued to an insulating rod, and the position of sphere B is adjustable. The insulating parts need to be dry, and a warm **air** blower is useful for this purpose.

Both spheres are fully charged by contact with the charged dome of a Van-de-Graaff generator, and a lamp is arranged to cast a shadow of sphere A on a vertical sheet of graph paper. The centre, or preferably a vertical edge, of the shadow is marked on the graph paper. Sphere B is now brought up to the suspended sphere A until the latter is deflected, both spheres being at the same horizontal level. A quick series of readings of the shadow deflection D of sphere A for various values of the shadow distance R between the spheres are recorded. It should be noted that $D \propto d$, where d is the actual deflection of sphere A, and $R \propto r$, where r is the actual centre-to-centre distance between the spheres. If, in spite of precautions, there is still considerable leakage of charge from the spheres, then the spheres should be fully charged after each set of readings.

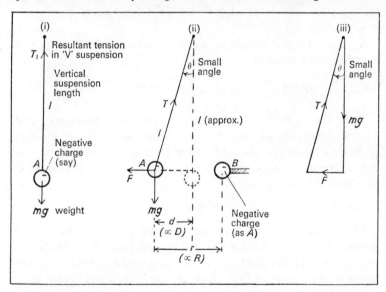

Fig 5.9 *Theory of method for the quantitative investigation of Coulomb's Law of Force*
    (i) *Charged sphere A in absence of B.* $T_1 = mg$
   (ii) *Sphere A repelled by B is in equilibrium under the action of three forces. Displacement of A = d ($\propto$ the shadow displacement D); distance between spheres = r ($\propto$ the shadow distance R)*
  (iii) *Triangle of Forces for the three forces in equilibrium*

The theory of this method, illustrated in fig 5.9, makes use of the triangle of forces theorem, which states that if three forces acting at a point are in equilibrium, then they can be represented in magnitude and direction by the three sides of a triangle taken in order. Since the two triangles in fig 5.9(ii) and (iii) are similar, it follows that for small angles of θ,

$$\frac{F}{mg} = \frac{d}{l}$$

$$\therefore \quad F = \frac{mg}{l}d \qquad\qquad \therefore \quad F \propto d \, (\propto D).$$

Hence the shadow deflection D is a measure of the force between the spheres, and of course R is a measure of r, the distance between the spheres. Assuming an inverse nth power law for the variation of the force with distance apart,

$$D = \frac{\text{const.}}{R^n} \quad \text{or} \quad \log D = \log \text{const.} - n \log R.$$

A graph of $\log D$ should be plotted against $\log R$. This gives a straight line of gradient -2.

$$\text{hence} \qquad F \propto \frac{1}{r^2}.$$

Using the method of charge sharing described previously, and always keeping the distance R at a constant value, it is found that D (hence F) is halved when the charge Q on sphere A is halved, and that D becomes a quarter of its original value when the charge Q on sphere B is also halved.

Therefore $\qquad\qquad F \propto Q_1 Q_2.$

Thus Coulomb's Law is obtained, which states that the force F between two point charges Q_1 and Q_2 separated by distance r is proportional to the product of the charges and inversely proportional to the square of their distance apart, the force acting along the line joining the charges.

Expressing Coulomb's Law as an equation requires the introduction of a constant of proportionality which is written $1/(4\pi\varepsilon)$. The factor 4π appears because SI units are rationalised and symmetry is spherical; the constant ε (epsilon) is a property of the medium between the point charges called the 'permittivity' of the medium.

Coulomb's Law equation becomes

$$F = \frac{1}{4\pi\,\varepsilon} \frac{Q_1\,Q_2}{r^2} \tag{5.2}$$

where F is the force in newtons
             Q is the charge in coulombs
             r is the distance between the charges in
              metres.

The derived unit of ε is farad metre^{-1}. From equation 5.2, the unit of $\varepsilon = \dfrac{C \times C}{N \times m \times m} = \dfrac{C}{V \times m} = \dfrac{F}{m}\,\dfrac{\text{(farad)}}{\text{(metre)}}$, the farad being shorthand for 1 coulomb per volt.

Permittivity of Free Space, ε_0

If the medium is a vacuum, then the permittivity constant is written ε_0 (epsilon nought). Its value in SI units could, in principle, be determined experimentally by measuring the force between two point charges of known magnitude and given distance apart in a vacuum, but because of the difficulty of leakage of charge from the spheres and of approximating to point charges, this is not a practical proposition for an accurate determination. Instead, formulae may be deduced from Coulomb's Law which lend themselves more readily to measurement, and experimental results using a capacitor give

$$\varepsilon_0 = 8\cdot85 \times 10^{-12} \text{ F m}^{-1} \quad \textbf{(p. 150).}$$

Worked Example

Calculate the force of attraction between two small spheres carrying charges of $+10^{-8}$ and -10^{-8} coulombs in a vacuum, the distance between their centres being 4 cm (take $1/(4\pi\,\varepsilon_0) = 9 \times 10^9$ numerically).

Using Coulomb's Law,

$$F = \frac{1}{4\pi\,\varepsilon_0} \frac{Q_1\,Q_2}{r^2} = 9 \times 10^9 \times \frac{10^{-8} \times (-10^{-8})}{(4 \times 10^{-2})^2}$$

$$\therefore \quad F = -\tfrac{9}{16} \times 10^{-3} \text{ N} \quad \therefore \quad F = -5\cdot6 \times 10^{-4} \text{ N}.$$

(The negative sign indicates a force of attraction.)
The student may wish to check that this force is of the same magnitude as the earth's gravitational pull on a mass of approximately 57 milligrams.

Cavendish's Proof of the Inverse Square Law

Some eighteen years prior to Coulomb's experiments, Joseph Priestley had shown experimentally that there is no detectable charge on the inside surface of a charged, hollow conductor and that there is no electric force inside a charged, hollow conductor. He proposed that this observation implied an inverse square law of force and in 1772 Henry Cavendish first demonstrated the truth of this hypothesis.

Consider a positively charged hollow conducting sphere, with a positive test charge placed at point P along a diameter of the sphere. Let the small cone marking out an area A_1 containing charge Q_1 at distance r_1 from P be extended backwards to mark out an area A_2

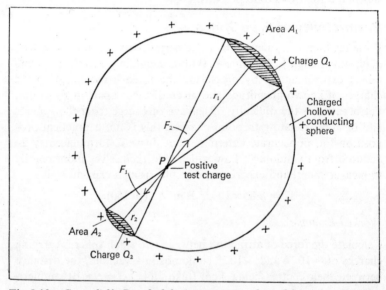

Fig 5.10 *Cavendish's Proof of the inverse square law of force, based on the observation that there is no resultant force inside a charged hollow conducting sphere i.e. $F_1 = F_2$*

containing charge Q_2 at distance r_2 from P (fig 5.10). The base areas of the cones are proportional to the squares of their distances from P, e.g. doubling r_1 doubles the radius of area A_1 and therefore quadruples the area of A_1.

$$\frac{A_1}{A_2} = \frac{r_1^{\,2}}{r_2^{\,2}}$$

Since by symmetry the electric charge distributes itself evenly over the surface, the quantity of charge is proportional to the base area of a cone.

$$\frac{Q_1}{Q_2} = \frac{r_1^2}{r_2^2} \qquad \text{(X)}$$

Now assuming an inverse nth power law of force, the forces on the test charge at P due to the two charge areas Q_1 and Q_2 are

$$F_1 \propto \frac{Q_1}{r_1^n} \qquad \text{and} \qquad F_2 \propto \frac{Q_2}{r_2^n}.$$

But the experimental observation is that $F_1 = F_2$,

$$\therefore \quad \frac{Q_1}{r_1^n} = \frac{Q_2}{r_2^n}, \qquad \text{and} \qquad \frac{Q_1}{Q_2} = \frac{r_1^n}{r_2^n}. \qquad \text{(Y)}$$

Other pairs of cones at P meet the surface of the sphere at an angle, but this angle is the same for both cones and the effect cancels.

Comparing equations (X) and (Y) shows that n must equal exactly 2 for there to be zero resultant force at any point inside a hollow charged conducting sphere, and more advanced mathematics extends the result to any closed surface, for example, a cylindrical 'ice-pail'.

Electric Field Strength, E

Coulomb's Law describes how the force between two stationary point charges Q_1 and Q_2 depends on the magnitudes of the charges, on their distance r apart and on the permittivity ε of the medium in which they are situated.

Suppose now that charge Q_1 begins to oscillate (say with simple harmonic motion) along a direction at right angles to the line joining Q_1 and Q_2 (see fig 5.11). How quickly does Q_2 'learn' that Q_1 is oscillating, that the distance between the charges is varying, and that the force between the charges must therefore also vary? Up to Faraday's time, it was generally thought that this 'information' was transmitted instantaneously, and this was the basis of the 'action-at-a-distance' model to explain the varying force on Q_2 (fig 5.11). Such a model does not, however, stand up to modern experimental test. If electrons oscillate rapidly at say 10^6 Hz in a transmitting aerial, then it is found that rapidly changing forces with a frequency of 10^6 Hz act on electrons in a receiving aerial distance l away after a time

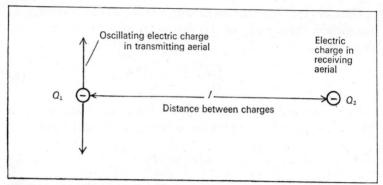

Fig 5.11 *The varying force on Q_2 due to the oscillating charge Q_1, occurs after a time interval $t = l/c$, where c is the velocity of electro-magnetic radiation*

interval $t = l/c$, where c is the velocity of electromagnetic radiation. The 'action-at-a-distance' model breaks down: action at a distance is not instantaneous.

The modern view introduces the concept of an 'electric field'. Such an electric field is said to exist in the space around an electric charge Q_1. If another charge Q_2 is situated in this field, then charge Q_2 experiences a force. In the above example, an oscillating charge Q_1 produces an oscillating electric field which is transmitted with the speed of electromagnetic radiation, and which acts with an oscillating force on charge Q_2. It is seen that the field theory requires us to say what shape and strength of field is produced by a certain configuration of charge, and what force that field will then produce on another charge placed in the field.

The electric field strength E at a particular point in an electric field is defined as being numerically equal to the force F exerted per unit charge placed at that point, i.e. $E = F$/unit charge, the unit of E being newton per coulomb. If a charge Q is placed at a point in an electric field where the field strength is E, then the force F on the charge is given by

$$F = Q E. \tag{5.3}$$

The positive direction of an electric field is taken as the direction in which the force acts on a positive charge placed in the field. Since electric field strength has magnitude and direction, it is a vector quantity.

Electric Field Strength due to an Isolated Point Charge

Consider a positive point charge Q situated in a medium of permittivity ε. To calculate the electric field strength E, at a point P, distance r from Q, imagine a unit positive charge $+1$ coulomb to be placed at P (fig 5.12). By Coulomb's Law, the force on the unit charge is

$$F = \frac{1}{4\pi\,\varepsilon}\,\frac{Q\times 1}{r^2}.$$

But E is defined as the force per unit charge

$$E = \frac{1}{4\pi\,\varepsilon}\,\frac{Q}{r^2}. \qquad (5.4)$$

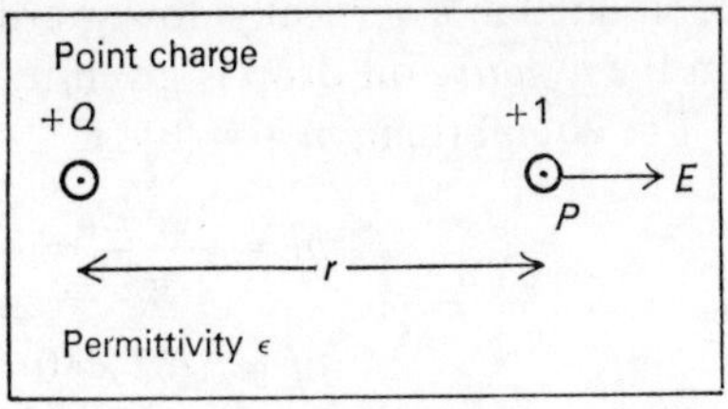

Point charge
$+Q$ $+1$
P $\longrightarrow E$
$\longleftarrow r \longrightarrow$
Permittivity ϵ

Fig 5.12 *The electric field strength due to an isolated point charge is given by* $E = \frac{1}{4\pi\epsilon}\cdot\frac{Q}{r_2}$

The direction of E is marked in fig 5.12. It should be noted that the strength of the field falls off with distance according to an inverse-square law. If the $+Q$ point charge were replaced by a $-Q$ point charge, then the field vector at P would point towards $-Q$ (unlike charges attract).

The analogy between various quantities in electrostatics and gravitation is an interesting one, and is illustrated in table 5.1.

Table 5.1. Comparison of electric and gravitational field quantities.

Electric field	Gravitational field
point charge Q	point mass m
electric field strength E (in newton coulomb^{-1})	gravitational field strength g (in newton kilogramme^{-1})
electric force $F = QE$	gravitational force $F = mg$
Coulomb's Law $F = \frac{1}{4\pi\,\varepsilon}\,\frac{Q_1 Q_2}{r^2}$	Newton's Law $F = G\frac{m_1 m_2}{r^2}$
attractive and repulsive forces exist	attractive forces ONLY exist

Worked Example

Calculate the mass of an oil drop carrying a charge of 10 electrons which just remains suspended in a vertical electric field of 10^5 newton coulomb^{-1} ($e = -1\cdot60 \times 10^{-19}$ C, $g = 9\cdot81$ N kg^{-1}).

For the negatively charged oil drop to remain suspended, it must be situated in a vertically downward electric field. The *upward* force on the *negative* oil drop is given by $10e\,E$.

For equilibrium, $m\,g = 10e\,E$

$$m = \frac{10e\,E}{g} = \frac{10 \times 1\cdot60 \times 10^{-19} \times 10^5}{9\cdot81}$$

$$\therefore \quad m = 1\cdot63 \times 10^{-14} \text{ kg}.$$

Electric Field Patterns

The *magnetic* field patterns near different configurations of current-carrying conductors is conveniently represented by the pattern of lines of *magnetic* flux (force), which can be illustrated experimentally by using iron filings or a small plotting compass. Similarly, lines of electric flux (force) can be used to represent *electric* field patterns, a line of electric flux being the direction in which a small positive test charge would move. Clearly iron filings cannot be used to illustrate the shape of an electric field because the iron would provide a conducting path between the static charges. However, it is found that semolina or very short (2 mm) lengths of hair or bristles suspended in castor oil in a glass dish show electric field patterns very well. Some thick copper wire is bent into suitable shapes to represent point, curved and plate electrodes and these are dipped into the ½ cm deep layer of fresh castor oil containing a little semolina. A 5 kV power pack, or preferably a Van-de-Graaff generator is connected to the electrodes and the semolina arranges itself into patterns similar to those illustrated in fig 5.13.

The shape of the electric field near the dome of a Van-de-Graaff generator, or between two parallel plates with a 5 kV power pack connected across them, may be illustrated by a small diamond-shaped paper indicator, which is free to rotate about a pin as axis, the pin being Sellotaped to an insulating rod. As the rod is moved, the paper pointer orientates itself in the direction of the electric field. No field is detected inside a hollow charged conductor. It follows, therefore, that electric flux lines start (say) on the surface of a positively charged conducting sphere, and end on a negatively charged conducting

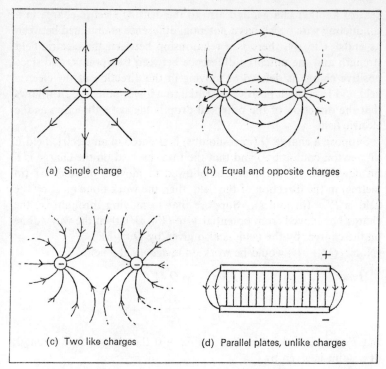

(a) Single charge

(b) Equal and opposite charges

(c) Two like charges

(d) Parallel plates, unlike charges

Fig 5.13   *Typical electric field patterns*

sphere, as in fig 5.13. Electric flux lines are not continuous. Magnetic flux lines, on the other hand, are continuous, and this is an important difference.

Electric Potential, V
Potential Gradient

Potential difference between two points in an electric field has been defined on p. 17 as the work done against electrical forces in taking unit charge from one point to the other. If W is the work done in transferring a charge of Q from one point in an electric field to another point, then the potential difference V between the points is given by $V = W/Q$

or $\qquad W = Q V.$ (p. 21)

This definition applies to an electric charge moving in the electric field of another charge, and also to the drifting electric charge in a conducting wire which has a potential difference maintained between its ends. Clearly, there is a relationship between the electric field strength and the potential difference between two points, and since positive charge is defined as moving in the direction of the electric field and from high positive potential to a lower potential, it follows that the direction of the potential drop is the same direction as the electric field.

Suppose a charge Q (in coulombs) is situated in an electric field E (in newton coulomb^{-1}) and that the force exerted on the charge is F (in newtons). If the charge is allowed to move a distance δx (in metres) in the direction of the field, then the work done on it by the field is $F \delta x$ (in joules). Suppose that in moving through δx, the charge has moved from potential V to $(V - \delta V)$, then the work done on the charge, by the field, is also given by $Q(-\delta V)$.
(Note: $Q(+\delta V)$ would be work done *against* the field.)

Hence

$$F \delta x = -Q \delta V$$

$$\therefore \quad \frac{F}{Q} = -\frac{\delta V}{\delta x}$$

but $F/Q = E$ and in the limit as $\delta x \to 0$ the electric field strength at a point is given by

$$E = -\frac{dV}{dx}. \tag{5.5}$$

The negative sign indicates a decrease in V as x increases in the positive direction of the field, and the ratio dV/dx is called the *potential gradient* measured in volt metre^{-1}. It follows that electric field strength can either be expressed in newton coulomb^{-1} or volt metre^{-1}, i.e. the units are equivalent.

Worked Example

What potential difference must be applied to two horizontal, parallel conducting plates, 1 cm apart, so that the electric field strength between the plates is 10^5 newton coulomb^{-1}?

Electric field strength = Potential Gradient

$$\therefore \quad E = \frac{\text{potential difference } V}{\text{distance apart } d}$$

hence $\qquad V = E\,d$

$$= 10^5\,\frac{N}{C} \times 10^{-2}\,m$$

$$= 10^3\,\frac{N\,m}{C}\,\left(\frac{J}{C}\right)$$

Potential difference required $= 1000$ V

Alternatively, 10^5 N C^{-1} $= 10^5$ V m^{-1} $= 10^3$ V cm^{-1}

Potential due to an Isolated Point Charge

Let the point charge $+Q$ be situated in a medium of permittivity ε. By definition, the potential at a point P, distance r from it, equals the work done in moving unit positive charge of $+1$ coulomb from infinity to P against the electric forces. Consider the unit positive charge, which must be assumed not to affect the field, to be moved

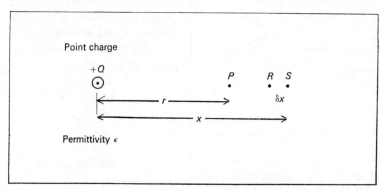

Fig 5.14 *The electric potential due to an isolated point charge is given by*
$$V = \frac{1}{4\pi\epsilon}\cdot\frac{Q}{r}$$

from S, distance x from $+Q$, through a small distance δx to R (see fig 5.14), assuming that the force F on the test charge stays constant over this incremental distance.

Work done on unit test charge $= F(-\delta x)$

$$= \frac{1}{4\pi\,\varepsilon}\,\frac{Q\times 1}{x^2}\,(-\delta x)$$

(the minus sign appears because δx is in the direction of decreasing values of x).

Total work done in bringing unit test charge from infinity to point P distance r from point charge $+Q$ is given by

$$\int_{\infty}^{r} -\frac{1}{4\pi\,\varepsilon}\frac{Q}{x^2}\,\mathrm{d}x = \frac{1}{4\pi\,\varepsilon}\frac{Q}{r}$$

$$\therefore\quad V = \frac{1}{4\pi\,\varepsilon}\cdot\frac{Q}{r}. \tag{5.6}$$

Potential due to an Isolated Conducting Sphere

An isolated charged conducting sphere, with its (say) positive charge uniformly distributed over its surface, has a radial pattern of electric flux lines, each line being perpendicular to the surface of the sphere (see fig 5.15). For any point P external to the sphere, the field pattern is the same as if all the charge were concentrated as a point charge at the centre of the sphere. Hence the potential V at point P, distance r from the centre of the sphere, carrying a charge Q, in a medium of permittivity ε, is given by

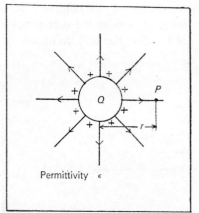

Permittivity ϵ

Fig 5.15 *The electric field pattern due to a charged isolated conducting sphere*

$$V = \frac{1}{4\pi\,\varepsilon}\frac{Q}{r}.$$

If $r = a$, where a is the radius of the sphere,

then $$V = \frac{1}{4\pi\,\varepsilon}\frac{Q}{a}. \tag{5.7}$$

At all points inside the sphere, the electric field strength is zero. Therefore no work is required to move a charge between them. It follows that the potential is the same at all internal points and is equal to the potential at the surface. Fig 5.16 illustrates the variation of E and V at points inside and outside a positively charged spherical conductor. It should be noted that the surfaces on which all points are at the same potential, called *equipotential* surfaces, are concentric

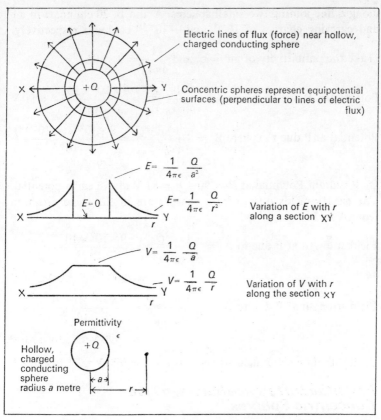

Electric lines of flux (force) near hollow, charged conducting sphere

Concentric spheres represent equipotential surfaces (perpendicular to lines of electric flux)

$E = \dfrac{1}{4\pi\epsilon}\dfrac{Q}{a^2}$

$E = 0$

$E = \dfrac{1}{4\pi\epsilon}\dfrac{Q}{r^2}$

Variation of E with r along a section X$\dot{\text{Y}}$

$V = \dfrac{1}{4\pi\epsilon}\dfrac{Q}{a}$

$V = \dfrac{1}{4\pi\epsilon}\dfrac{Q}{r}$

Variation of V with r along the section XY

Permittivity

Hollow, charged conducting sphere radius a metre

Fig 5.16 *Electric field strength E and electric potential V inside and outside a hollow, charged conducting sphere in a medium of permittivity* ϵ

for a spherical conductor, and that lines of electric flux (force) are always perpendicular to the equipotential surfaces.

Whereas electric field strength is a vector quantity, potential has either a positive or negative magnitude, but no direction. Potential is, therefore, a scalar quantity, and in calculations involving the resultant potential of several charges, potentials are summed by algebraic addition. The resultant electric field strength due to several charges must be calculated by vector addition.

Worked Example

Find the potential and electric field strength at a point P midway along a line joining two small spheres, A and B, 20 cm apart in air and carrying charges of 10^{-9} and -10^{-10} coulomb respectively.

(Take the permittivity of air $= \varepsilon_0$ and $\dfrac{1}{4\pi\,\varepsilon_0} = 9 \times 10^9$.)

Potential at P due to sphere A $= \dfrac{1}{4\pi\,\varepsilon_0}\,\dfrac{Q}{r_A} = \dfrac{9\times 10^9 \times 10^{-9}}{10^{-1}} = 90\ \text{V}$

Potential at P due to sphere B $= \dfrac{1}{4\pi\,\varepsilon_0}\,\dfrac{-Q}{r_B} = \dfrac{9\times 10^9 \times (-10^{-10})}{10^{-1}}$

$$= -9\ \text{V}$$

$\therefore$ Resultant Potential at $P = 90 - 9 = 81$ V above earth potential. The electric fields due to both charges are in the same direction from A to B.

Field strength at P due to A $= \dfrac{1}{4\pi\,\varepsilon_0}\,\dfrac{Q}{r_A{}^2} = \dfrac{9\times 10^9 \times 10^{-9}}{10^{-2}}$

$$= 900\ \text{V m}^{-1} \text{ towards B}$$

Field strength at P due to B $= \dfrac{1}{4\pi\,\varepsilon_0}\,\dfrac{-Q}{r_B{}^2} = \dfrac{9\times 10^9 \times (-10^{-10})}{10^{-2}}$

$$= -90\ \text{V m}^{-1} \text{ towards B}$$

$\therefore$ Resultant electric field strength at P $= 990$ V m^{-1} towards B

Potential Difference between Two Concentric Spheres

Consider two concentric conducting spheres of radius a and b respectively, situated in a medium of permittivity ε (fig 5.17). Suppose a charge $+Q$ is placed on the inner sphere and the outer sphere is earthed. Then, by induction, the inner surface of the outer sphere gets a charge $-Q$ (the outer surface is earthed). The potential due to charge $-Q$ is $\dfrac{1}{4\pi\,\varepsilon}\,\dfrac{(-Q)}{b}$ everywhere inside the larger sphere and the potential of the inner sphere due to charge $+Q$ on its surface is $\dfrac{1}{4\pi\,\varepsilon}\,\dfrac{Q}{a}$. By algebraic addition, the total potential at the surface of the inner sphere

$$= \dfrac{1}{4\pi\,\varepsilon}\,\dfrac{Q}{a} + \dfrac{1}{4\pi\,\varepsilon}\,\dfrac{(-Q)}{b}.$$

This is, in fact, the potential difference between the spheres since the outer sphere is earthed at zero potential. Therefore the p.d. between two concentric spheres as in fig 5.17 is given by:

$$V = \frac{Q}{4\pi \, \varepsilon} \left(\frac{1}{a} - \frac{1}{b} \right). \qquad (5.8)$$

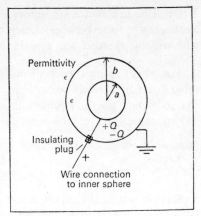

Fig 5.17 *The potential difference between two concentric spheres, the inner with charge $+Q$ and the outer one earthed, is given by*

$$V = \frac{Q}{4\pi\epsilon} \left(\frac{1}{a} - \frac{1}{b} \right)$$

Inspection of equation 5.8 shows that the effect of surrounding a sphere (radius a) by a concentric earthed outer sphere (radius b), is to decrease the potential of the inner sphere when it carries a given charge $+ Q$ (in coulombs). Conversely, a concentric sphere arrangement gives the inner sphere the capacity to hold more electric charge at a given potential. The study of the capacity of conductors to carry electric charge, per unit potential, is the subject of chapter 6.

Questions

(Take $g = 9 \cdot 81 \text{ m s}^{-2} = 9 \cdot 81 \text{ N kg}^{-1}$.)

1. A fellow student proposes the hypothesis that when two insulated conducting spheres A and B are in contact, and a negatively charged polythene strip is held near A, there is a *flow of electrons* from A to B. How would you help him to test this hypothesis experimentally? What theories would you use and what assumptions would you make?

2. Describe Faraday's ice-pail experiment and explain carefully the conclusions which may be drawn from it. Explain a practical application of one of the facts demonstrated by this experiment.

(A.E.B. part)

3. Describe in detail a laboratory experiment which leads to Coulomb's law of force between electric charges. Illustrate your account with suitable sketches and explain the theory of the method.

4. Two small spheres, each of mass 0·5 g, are suspended from the same point by threads 50 cm long. When the spheres are equally charged, they are in equilibrium with their centres 2 cm apart. Taking the earth's gravitational field strength as 10 newton kilogramme^{-1}, calculate the charge on each sphere. (Take $\dfrac{1}{4\pi\,\varepsilon_0} = 9 \times 10^9$ numerically.)

5. State in words the experimental results contained in Coulomb's law of force between electric charges.

Express the law as an equation, and explain the form of the constant.

The force of repulsion between two negatively charged spheres, one of which carries half the charge of the other, is 10^{-4} newton when the centres of the spheres are 4 cm apart in air. Calculate the charge carried by each sphere.

(Take the permittivity of air $= \varepsilon_0 = 8\cdot85 \times 10^{-12}$ F m^{-1}.)

6. How may an insulated metal sphere be charged positively by induction? Explain the action of an electrophorus.

Name one major advantage in using an electrophorus as a simple electrical machine.

State Coulomb's Law of Force for point charges.

The charge on an electron is $1\cdot60 \times 10^{-19}$ coulomb, and the mass of an α-particle is $6\cdot68 \times 10^{-27}$ kg. Show that if two α-particles are 10^{-10} cm apart, the electrostatic repulsion force between them is about 3×10^{35} times the gravitational attraction between them.

$$\frac{1}{4\pi\,\varepsilon_0} = 9 \times 10^9 \text{ newton-metre}^2 \text{ coulomb}^{-2}$$

$$G = 6\cdot67 \times 10^{-11} \text{ newton-metre}^2 \text{ kilogramme}^{-2}$$

(B.Ed. Aberdeen)

7. What is meant by the 'electric field strength' at a point in an electric field?

Derive an expression for the electric field strength E at a distance r

from a point charge $+Q$ situated in a medium of permittivity ε.

Calculate (a) the electric field strength at a point P, 1 cm from a point charge of 10^{-8} coulomb, in air and (b) the force at P on an ionised air molecule carrying one excess electron. (Electronic charge $e = 1 \cdot 60 \times 10^{-19}$ C; take the permittivity of air $= \varepsilon_0$ and

$$\frac{1}{4\pi \, \varepsilon_0} = 9 \times 10^9 \text{ numerically.)}$$

8. Define the terms (a) Electric field strength, (b) Electric potential and show how these concepts are related.

In what units are they measured?

On what factors does the force between two point charges depend? How could the dependence on these factors be verified experimentally?

Four point charges are held in air at the corners of a square going round the square in a clockwise direction; they are $+Q$, $-3Q$, $+2Q$, and $-6Q$. What is the field strength and the electric potential at the centre of the square, if $Q = 10^{-9}$ coulomb and the sides of the square are of length 10 cm?

$$\frac{1}{4\pi \, \varepsilon_0} = 9 \times 10^9 \text{ newton-metre}^2 \text{ coulomb}^{-2}$$

(B.Ed. Aberdeen)

9. What is meant by a 'line of electric flux (force)'?

Why must lines of electric flux always leave or enter a charged conductor at right angles?

Describe an experiment which enables electric field patterns to be made visible, and sketch the shape of the electric field around two equal and opposite charges a short distance apart.

10. Describe, with the aid of a labelled diagram, a Van-de-Graaff generator, explaining the physical principles of its action.

The high-voltage terminal of such a generator consists of a spherical conducting shell of radius 50 cm. Estimate the maximum potential to which it can be raised in air for which electrical breakdown occurs when the electric intensity exceeds 30 000 volt cm^{-1}.

State *two* ways in which this maximum potential could be increased. (J.M.B.)

11. What do you understand by an equi-potential surface? Justify

the statement 'conducting surfaces are always equi-potential surfaces in electrostatics'. In what circumstances is a conducting surface not an equi-potential surface?

12. An isolated conducting spherical shell of radius 10 cm, *in vacuo*, carries a positive charge of 1.0×10^{-7} coulomb. Calculate (*a*) the electric field strength, (*b*) the potential, at a point on the surface of the conductor. Sketch a graph to show how one of these quantities varies with distance along a radius from the centre to a point well outside the spherical shell. Point out the main features of the graph. (Electric space const. = $\varepsilon_0 = 8.85 \times 10^{-12}$ farad m^{-1})   (J.M.B.)

13. Explain the meaning of the terms electric potential and electric field strength.

A positively charged glass sphere is placed on the axis of an insulated metal rod some distance from one of its ends. Account for the resulting charge distribution over the metal rod.

How do you reconcile the charge distribution on the metal rod with the fact that the only free charges in a metal are electrons?

Sketch freehand graphs showing the form of the variation of (*a*) the electric potential and (*b*) the electric field strength along the axis of the metal rod from the surface of the glass sphere, through the rod to a distant point.

How and why is the electric field between the glass sphere and the metal rod changed if the metal rod is earthed?   (O. & C.)

14. Explain what is meant by the electrical potential at a point and obtain the expression for the potential at a point distance x from an isolated positive point charge of magnitude Q. Deduce the relationship between the strength of the electrical field and the potential gradient at a given point in the field.

(*a*) The electric field near the surface of the earth is 100 V m^{-1}. Calculate the surface density of charge on the earth's surface.

(*b*) If the potential gradient exceeds 30 000 V cm^{-1} a breakdown discharge takes place in air at s.t.p. Calculate the maximum radius of a sphere which will discharge to the air if its potential is 600 V. (Take the permittivity of air = $\varepsilon_0 = 8.85 \times 10^{-12}$ F m^{-1}.) (A.E.B.)

15. Derive an expression for the p.d., V, between two concentric spheres of radii a and b respectively ($b > a$) situated in a medium of permittivity ε, when a charge of $+Q$ is placed on the inner sphere and the outer surface of the larger sphere is earthed.

Given that $a = 3$ cm and $b = 4$ cm, determine the number of electrons which need to be removed from the inner sphere to produce a p.d. of 3 volts between the spheres in air. (Assume that the permittivity of air $= \varepsilon_0$ and $\dfrac{1}{4\pi\,\varepsilon_0} = 9 \times 10^9$ numerically, and that the electronic charge $e = 1 \cdot 60 \times 10^{-19}$ coulomb.)

Chapter 6

Capacitance and Capacitors

Capacitance, *C*

Momentary Currents

In the 'free electron' theory for metals (chapter 1 p. 14), an electric current is pictured as a net drift of electrons through the atomic lattice of the conducting wire. This electron drift is the result of a potential gradient or electric field along the length of the conductor, exerting a net force on the electrons in a direction from negative to positive potential. If a variable 5 kV power supply is connected in series with a 50 MΩ safety resistance, two identical light-beam galvanometers and a length of conducting wire XZ (see fig 6.1), then the net electron drift is indicated on the galvanometers as a steady current (conventional) flowing in direction XZ. The conducting wire XZ is suitably made up of two insulated 4 mm leads XY_1 and Y_2Z,

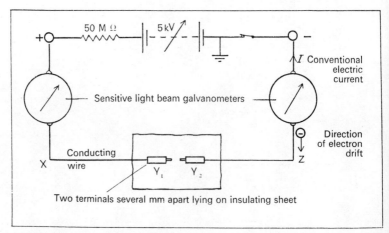

Fig 6.1   *Circuit for the demonstration of steady and momentary currents*

with ends Y_1 and Y_2 connected together and lying on an insulating sheet of polythene.

Suppose that the electric circuit (fig 6.1) is broken and contacts Y_1 and Y_2 are placed several mm apart on the insulating sheet. When the power supply is switched on (2 kV is suitable), there is now no detectable steady current, but there is a momentary 'fling' of the light-beam galvanometers on the 'direct or ballistic' setting. Since the first throw θ of a ballistic galvanometer is directly proportional to the pulse of charge Q, it follows that there is a momentary current flow when the power supply is switched on (and off). The direction of the deflections of the galvanometers is such that the momentary currents (equal on both galvanometers) are due to electrons piling up on Y_2 and electrons moving away from Y_1, leaving an equal positive charge. Presumably the electric charge builds up on Y_1 and Y_2 until the potential difference between the points equals the terminal potential difference of the power supply. This hypothesis may be tested by noting the 'throw' when 1 kV, 2 kV and 3 kV are applied in turn to terminals Y_1 and Y_2. In a typical experiment the first 'throw' on a light-beam ballistic galvano-

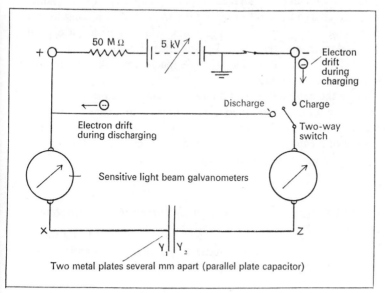

Fig 6.2 *Demonstration of momentary charging and discharging currents using a parallel-plate capacitor*

meter was 0·5 mm, 1·0 mm and 1·5 mm respectively, indicating that *the charge* Q *on each point is proportional to the applied potential difference* V.

How might the capacity of points Y_1 and Y_2 to hold charge be increased for a given p.d.: by giving the electrons a larger area over which to pile up? Fig 6.2 shows the plug ends Y_1 and Y_2 replaced by two parallel metal plates Y_1 and Y_2 to which electrical connections can be made and which are separated by the same distance (several mm) as the points in the above experiment. The two-way switch is moved to the 'charge' position and the power supply is switched on. The 'throws' of the light-beam galvanometers are considerably larger now for a given applied p.d. during charging and discharging, indicating that this arrangement does indeed have a larger capacity to hold (or store) charge at a given p.d. Varying the magnitude of the applied p.d. confirms that the charge Q on each plate is proportional to the applied p.d. V

i.e. $\qquad Q \propto V$

or $\qquad Q = CV \qquad\qquad\qquad$ (6.1)

where C (capacitance) is a measure of the capacity of the conductor to store charge per unit potential difference. C is a constant for a particular arrangement of conductors, which is called a capacitor or condenser, e.g. the parallel plate arrangement above is called a parallel plate capacitor. The unit of capacitance is the coulomb/volt, which is called the *farad*.

Since the coulomb is such a large amount of charge, the farad is a very large unit, and in practice capacitances are expressed in microfarads ($1\ \mu F = 10^{-6}$ F) or picofarads ($1\ pF = 10^{-12}$ F). The capacitance of a capacitor is 1 microfarad if 1 microcoulomb of charge is stored at a potential difference of 1 volt.

Capacitance of an Isolated Spherical Conductor

If an isolated spherical conductor of radius a situated in a medium of permittivity ε, is given a charge $+Q$, then the potential V at its surface with respect to earth potential is given by equation 5.7 as

$$V = \frac{1}{4\pi\,\varepsilon}\,\frac{Q}{a}.$$

But
$$C = \frac{Q}{V}$$

$$\therefore \quad C = 4\pi \, \varepsilon \, a \tag{6.2}$$

i.e. the capacitance of a sphere is proportional to its radius.

Worked Example

A conducting sphere of diameter 30 cm (e.g. the dome of a Van-de-Graaff generator) is charged to a potential of 100 000 V with respect to earth potential. Calculate the charge on the sphere assuming it to be situated in air.

(Take the permittivity of air $= \varepsilon_0 = 8 \cdot 85 \times 10^{-12} \, \text{F m}^{-1}$.)

The radius of the sphere $\quad a = 1 \cdot 5 \times 10^{-1} \, \text{m}$

$\therefore$ Capacitance of sphere $C = 4\pi \, \varepsilon_0 \, a$

$$= 4\pi \times 8 \cdot 85 \times 10^{-12} \times 1 \cdot 5 \times 10^{-1}$$

$$= 16 \cdot 7 \times 10^{-12} \, \text{F} \quad \text{(or 16·7 pF)}.$$

If $V = 10^5$ V

charge on sphere $\quad Q = CV$

$$= 16 \cdot 7 \times 10^{-12} \times 10^5$$

$$= 1 \cdot 67 \times 10^{-6} \, \text{C} \quad \text{(or 1·67 } \mu\text{C)}.$$

Note: Dry air breaks down as an insulator when the potential gradient is about 30 000 V cm^{-1}. If an earthed sphere approaches to within approximately 3 cm of the above sphere (charged to a potential of 100 000 V), then the electric charge ($= 1 \cdot 67 \, \mu C$) 'jumps' across the gap in the form of a spark.

Capacitance of a Parallel-plate Capacitor

The potential difference between two concentric conducting spheres of radii a and b respectively (see fig 5.17) situated in a medium of permittivity ε, with charge $+ Q$ (in coulombs) on the inner sphere and charge $- Q$ induced on the inner surface of the outer sphere (with the outer surface of the larger sphere earthed), is given by equation 5.8

i.e. $$V = \frac{Q}{4\pi \, \varepsilon} \left(\frac{1}{a} - \frac{1}{b} \right)$$

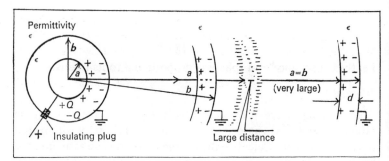

Fig 6.3 *A parallel-plate capacitor is a section of a greatly expanded concentric sphere capacitor*

$$\text{or} \qquad V = \frac{Q}{4\pi\,\varepsilon}\,\frac{(b-a)}{a\,b}.$$

If the concentric spheres are made very large keeping the distance apart $d = (b-a)$ constant (see fig 6.3), then a and b are very large and nearly equal, so that in the limit $a\,b = a^2$ to a good approximation

$$\therefore \quad V = \frac{Q}{4\pi\,\varepsilon}\,\frac{d}{a^2}$$

and the capacitance of the very large concentric spheres

$$C = \frac{Q}{V} = \frac{4\pi\,\varepsilon\,a^2}{d}.$$

Since the surface area of either sphere may be taken as $4\pi\,a^2$, the capacitance per unit area $= \dfrac{\varepsilon}{d}$ (in F m^{-2}.)

A parallel-plate capacitor may be regarded as a small part of such a very large concentric sphere capacitor, and if the parallel plates have a common area (area of plates facing each other) A at distance d apart in a medium of permittivity ε,

$$\text{then} \qquad C = \frac{\varepsilon\,A}{d}. \tag{6.3}$$

It follows that $\quad \dfrac{Q}{V} = \dfrac{\varepsilon\,A}{d}\quad$ or $\quad Q = \dfrac{V\,\varepsilon\,A}{d}.$

This latter formula may be investigated experimentally using the apparatus in fig 6.2 by noting the first 'throw' of the light-beam galvanometer ($\propto Q$) when (*i*) the permittivity ε is altered by filling the gap with paper or glass or other insulators (here called dielectrics), (*ii*) the common area A is varied, (*iii*) the distance d between the plates is varied. The experimental results confirm the variation of C with each of the factors ε, A and d as in equation 6.3.

Relative Permittivity, ε_r

It has been observed that when the gap in a parallel-plate capacitor is completely filled with an insulating material (dielectric), that the capacitance increases. The relative permittivity ε_r of a dielectric is defined by

$$\varepsilon_r = \frac{C}{C_0} \tag{6.4}$$

where C is the capacitance of a capacitor with the dielectric between its plates and C_0 is the capacitance of the same capacitor with a vacuum between its plates. Substituting for C and C_0 using equation 6.3,

$$\varepsilon_r = \frac{C}{C_0} = \frac{\varepsilon\, A/d}{\varepsilon_0\, A/d}$$

i.e.
$$\varepsilon_r = \frac{\varepsilon}{\varepsilon_0}. \tag{6.5}$$

Relative permittivity is therefore a dimensionless quantity and it has no units. For air at atmospheric pressure $\varepsilon_r = 1\cdot00054$, which is so nearly equal to 1 that for most purposes the capacitance of an air capacitor is equivalent to that of a capacitor in free space, and ε_{air} may be taken equal to ε_0 to a very good approximation. Some typical values of ε_r for various dielectrics are given in table 6.1.

Dielectric (at 293K)	Relative permittivity ε_r
Vacuum	1·00000
Air (1 atm)	1·00054
Paper (dry)	1·9–2·4
Glass	4·0–7·5
Polythene	2·3
Castor oil	4·5
Water (pure)	80

Table 6.1

Values of the relative permittivity ε_r (dielectric constant) for some common materials.

Dielectrics, Polarisation

How does a dielectric increase the capacity of a capacitor to store extra charge at a given applied potential difference? The effect of the dielectric must be to reduce the potential difference between the plates, so that the external power supply can then 'pump' more electrons round the external circuit until the extra charge on the plates makes the p.d. between the plates again equal to the applied p.d. The only factor which can reduce the p.d. in some way is the action of the electric field between the charged plates on the molecules of the dielectric. That is the hypothesis, and the action might be as follows: To reduce the positive potential of the positively charged plate, some negative charge (having negative potential near it) must appear near the plate; similarly, to make the negative potential of the negatively charged plate slightly less negative, some positive charge (having positive potential near it) must appear near that plate.

Consider a non-polar molecule (see fig 6.4). Such a molecule has the centre of gravity (C.G.) of its positive charges on the nuclei and

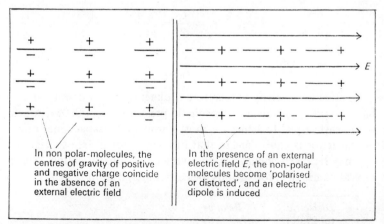

In non polar-molecules, the centres of gravity of positive and negative charge coincide in the absence of an external electric field

In the presence of an external electric field E, the non-polar molecules become 'polarised or distorted', and an electric dipole is induced

Fig 6.4 *Schematic diagrams of non-polar molecules in the absence and presence of an external electric field*

the centre of gravity of its negative electron clouds coincident in the absence of an external electric field. When an external electric field is applied, such a molecule becomes *distorted* because the C.G. of the positive charge is slightly displaced in the positive direction of the field, and the C.G. of the negative charge is slightly displaced against the direction of the field, until the force due to any displaced charge is equal and opposite to the force on the molecule due to the external field. Such a distorted molecule is said to be polarised and is the equivalent of an *electric dipole* (see fig 6.4). An electric dipole consists of a net positive and a net negative charge, separated slightly, but bound together.

Under the influence of the external electric field, the 'induced dipoles' align themselves in the field direction, and the dielectric

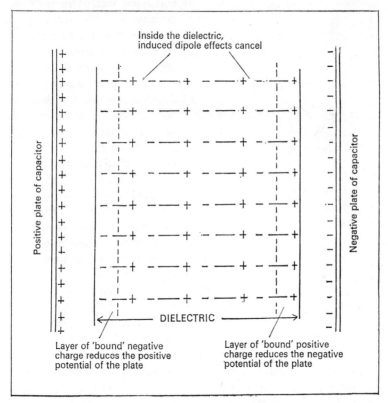

Fig 6.5 *Schematic diagram of the action of a dielectric in increasing the capacitance of a capacitor*

between the charged plates of the capacitor may be pictured as in fig 6.5. Inside the dielectric, the positive and negative ends of adjacent molecules neutralise each other's effects, but at the surfaces of the dielectric sheet there is a layer of 'bound' charge. Near the positively charged plate the 'bound' charge is negative; near the negatively charged plate the 'bound' charge is positive. This was the basic requirement to explain the action of a dielectric in increasing the capacitance of a capacitor.

The high relative permittivity ε_r of water is due to the fact that the H_2O molecule is polar, i.e. it is a permanent electric dipole because the relative position of the oxygen and hydrogen atoms makes one 'end' of the molecule positive and the other 'end' negative, even in the absence of an external electric field. The effect of an external field of strength E is to cause a certain degree of alignment of these dipoles depending on the strength of E (analogous to the alignment of Amperian current loops in an external magnetic field B). Superimposed on this is the 'induced dipole' as for nonpolar molecules, so that the total 'bound' charge on the surfaces of the dielectric is large compared with non-polar molecules. The considerable forces involved when a vertical stream of water from a tap passes through a non-uniform electric field of a charged polythene strip held close to the water are easily demonstrated (see fig 6.6). Again this is similar to a paramagnetic substance, where molecules having permanent electromagnetic moments move into the stronger part of a non-uniform magnetic field.

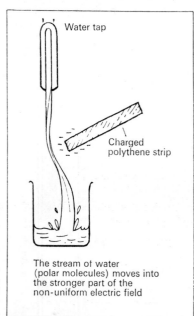

Water tap

Charged polythene strip

The stream of water (polar molecules) moves into the stronger part of the non-uniform electric field

Fig 6.6 *The action of a non-uniform electric field on a liquid having polar (permanent dipole) molecules, e.g. H_2O*

Energy Stored in a Charged Capacitor

Suppose an initially uncharged capacitor of capacitance C is connected to an appropriate power supply, and that at some instant during the charging process, the potential difference between the capacitor plates is V. If a further small increment of charge δQ

is 'pushed' on to the plates by the external supply, the energy transformed is measured by the electrical work done $= V\,\delta Q$. The increase in charge δQ will raise the p.d. of the capacitor by δV where $\delta Q = C\,\delta V$.

$$\therefore \quad \text{Work done} = C\,V\,\delta V.$$

The total energy transformed into electrical potential energy in the dielectric when the capacitor carries a charge Q at p.d. V is given by

$$E = \int_0^V C\,V\,\delta V = \tfrac{1}{2}\,C\,V^2$$

Using $Q = C\,V$

$$E = \tfrac{1}{2}\,C\,V^2 = \tfrac{1}{2}\,Q\,V = \tfrac{1}{2}\,\frac{Q^2}{C}. \qquad (6.6)$$

Worked Example

An electrolytic capacitor has a capacitance of 50 μF. It is charged through a safety resistor of 100 kΩ (say) to a p.d. of 240 V. (About 30 seconds should be allowed for this process.) Calculate (i) the charge on the plates, (ii) the electrical energy stored.

(i) Charge $\quad Q = C\,V \quad = 5 \times 10^{-5} \times 2{\cdot}4 \times 10^2$

$$= 1{\cdot}2 \times 10^{-2}\ \text{C}$$

(ii) Energy $\quad E = \tfrac{1}{2}\,Q\,V \quad = \tfrac{1}{2} \times 1{\cdot}2 \times 10^{-2} \times 2{\cdot}4 \times 10^2$

$$= 1{\cdot}44\ \text{J}$$

Note: If the above fully charged capacitor is discharged through a 240 V 15 W mains lamp (not using the safety resistor), there is a flash of light as the electrical potential energy in the dielectric is transformed into heat and light energy. Hence the initial rate of transformation of energy (i.e. power) is of the order of 10 W for a fraction of a second.

Capacitors in Series and in Parallel

Capacitors are said to be connected in *series* when the second plate of one capacitor is joined to the first plate of the next one, as in fig 6.7, which shows three capacitors having capacitances C_1, C_2 and C_3. When a p.d. V is applied, a charge $+Q$ on the first plate of the

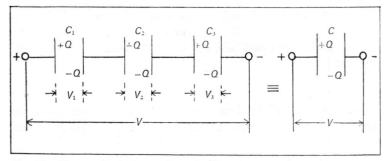

Fig 6.7 *The resultant capacitance C of capacitors connected in series is given by* $\dfrac{1}{C} = \dfrac{1}{C_1} + \dfrac{1}{C_2} + \dfrac{1}{C_3} \cdots$

first capacitor induces a charge $-Q$ on the second plate, so that a charge $+Q$ appears on the first plate of the second capacitor and so on, until the charge on the second plate of the last capacitor is $-Q$. Each capacitor has the same charge and the potential differences across individual capacitors are given by

$$V_1 = \frac{Q}{C_1} \qquad V_2 = \frac{Q}{C_2} \qquad V_3 = \frac{Q}{C_3}.$$

But the total p.d.

$$V = V_1 + V_2 + V_3$$

$$\therefore V = \frac{Q}{C_1} + \frac{Q}{C_2} + \frac{Q}{C_3}.$$

If C is the capacitance of a single capacitor which could replace the series combination, then it would have to carry charge Q at a p.d. V, so that

$$V = \frac{Q}{C}.$$

Substituting, $\qquad \dfrac{Q}{C} = \dfrac{Q}{C_1} + \dfrac{Q}{C_2} + \dfrac{Q}{C_3}$

$\therefore$ For capacitors in *series*,

$$\frac{1}{C} = \frac{1}{C_1} + \frac{1}{C_2} + \frac{1}{C_3}. \tag{6.7}$$

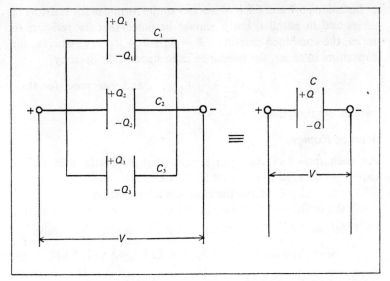

Fig 6.8 *The resultant capacitance C of capacitors connected in parallel is given by* $C = C_1 + C_2 + C_3 \ldots$

Capacitors are said to be connected in *parallel* when the first plate of each capacitor is connected to a common point, the second plate of each being connected to a second common point, as in fig 6.8 which shows three capacitors having capacitances C_1, C_2 and C_3. The p.d. V, applied between the common points, is the same for each of the capacitors and the charges stored are given by

$$Q_1 = C_1 V \quad Q_2 = C_2 V \quad Q_3 = C_3 V.$$

But the total charge Q stored on the parallel arrangement is given

by $$Q = Q_1 + Q_2 + Q_3$$

$$\therefore \quad Q = C_1 V + C_2 V + C_3 V.$$

If C is the capacitance of a single capacitor which could replace the parallel combination, then it would have to carry charge Q at a p.d. V, so that $\quad Q = C V$

Substituting, $C V = C_1 V + C_2 V + C_3 V.$

$\therefore$ For capacitors in *parallel*,

$$C = C_1 + C_2 + C_3. \tag{6.8}$$

149

Equations 6.7 and 6.8 look similar to the formulae for resistors in series and in parallel, but it should be noted that for resistors in series, the combined resistance $R = R_1 + R_2 + R_3, \ldots$, whereas for capacitors in series, the combined capacitance C is given by

$$\frac{1}{C} = \frac{1}{C_1} + \frac{1}{C_2} + \frac{1}{C_3} \ldots \text{ and vice versa for the}$$

parallel combinations.

Worked Example

An uncharged 2 μF capacitor is connected in parallel with a 1 μF capacitor, charged to a p.d. of 50 V. Calculate
    (*i*) the final p.d. across the capacitor combination and
    (*ii*) the initial and final energies. Comment on the results in (*ii*).

(*i*) Total capacitance of the 1 μF and 2 μF capacitors in parallel

$$C = C_1 + C_2 = 1\ \mu\text{F} + 2\ \mu\text{F} = 3\ \mu\text{F}\ (= 3 \times 10^{-6}\ \text{F})$$

The initial charge on the 1 μF capacitor

$$Q_1 = C_1 V_1 = 10^{-6} \times 50 = 5 \times 10^{-5}\ C.$$

By the law of conservation of charge, this is now the total charge on both capacitors, i.e. $Q = Q_1$,

$$\therefore\ \text{Final p.d.}\ V = \frac{Q}{C} = \frac{5 \times 10^{-5}}{3 \times 10^{-6}} = \frac{50}{3} = 16 \cdot 7\ \text{V}$$

(*ii*) Initial energy $\frac{1}{2} Q_1 V_1 = \frac{1}{2} \times 5 \times 10^{-5} \times 50$

$$= 1 \cdot 25 \times 10^{-3}\ \text{J}$$

Final energy $\frac{1}{2} Q V = \frac{1}{2} \times 5 \times 10^{-5} \times 50/3$

$$= 0 \cdot 42 \times 10^{-3}\ \text{J}$$

The final energy is less than the initial energy, the difference being the energy which must have been transformed into another form when the capacitors were connected, and charge flowed in the connecting wires. Most of the energy would be transformed into heat energy, but some may have been radiated from the connecting wires in the form of radio waves.

Determination of the Permittivity of Air

The capacitance C of a parallel plate air capacitor of common area A and distance d apart, is given by equation 6.3,

$$\text{i.e.} \quad C = \frac{\varepsilon_{air} \, A}{d}$$

where ε_{air} is the permittivity of air.

If a potential difference V is applied to the capacitor, the charge Q which is stored on it is given by $Q = C V$ (equation 6.1). During discharge, that is the quantity of charge which also flows in the discharge circuit.

Suppose that such a parallel plate capacitor is charged and discharged repeatedly at a rate of f times per second by using a vibrating charge-discharge switch, as in fig 6.9. The charging circuit contains a 120 V dry battery or variable smoothed H.T. supply with a high

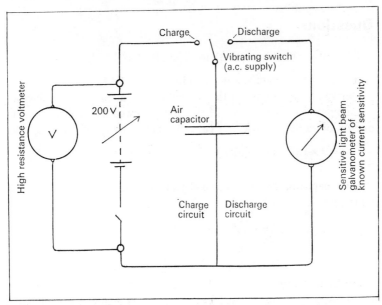

Fig 6.9 *Circuit for the determination of the permittivity of air* ($\varepsilon_{air} = \varepsilon_0 = 8\cdot85 \times 10^{-12} \mathrm{Fm}^{-1}$)

resistance voltmeter. A sensitive light-beam galvanometer of known current sensitivity measures the rate of flow of charge I in amperes in the discharge circuit, given by $I = f Q$ or $I = f C V$.

But $$\varepsilon_{air} = \frac{C \, d}{A}$$

by substituting, $$\varepsilon_{\text{air}} = \frac{I\,d}{f\,VA}.\qquad(6.9)$$

In practice the parallel plates of the capacitor need to be flat and sufficiently rigid to give constant separation when used with Perspex spacers about 2 mm thick. The charge-discharge switch may be operated from the 50 Hz mains supply, or from a calibrated frequency generator of sufficient power. It is important that all insulators are dry.

Within the limits of experimental error, the above determination of ε_{air} may be taken as a determination of ε_0, the permittivity of free space, for which the accepted value is $8\cdot85 \times 10^{-12}$ F m^{-1}.

Questions

(Take $g = 9\cdot81$ m s^{-2} = $9\cdot81$ N kg^{-1}.)

1. Define (a) capacitance of a conductor, (b) the farad.

Derive an expression for the capacitance of a spherical conductor.

Calculate the capacitance of the earth, viewed as a spherical conductor of radius 6400 km. (Take the permittivity of air $= \varepsilon_0$ and $\dfrac{1}{4\pi\,\varepsilon_0} = 9 \times 10^9$ numerically.)

2. The capacitance of a parallel-plate capacitor is given by the equation

$$C = \frac{\varepsilon\,A}{d}.$$

(a) Write down a consistent set of units for each physical quantity in the equation.

(b) Sketch the pattern of electric flux lines between two charged parallel plates.

(c) Explain why the equation is not strictly accurate.

(d) Describe how you would investigate the factors on which the capacitance of a parallel-plate capacitor depends.

3. A parallel-plate capacitor has circular plates of 8·0 cm radius and 1·0 mm separation. If a p.d. of 100 volt is applied, calculate:

(a) the charge on the plates in air;

(b) the charge on the plates with a dielectric, of relative permittivity = 5, between the plates;

(c) the number of electrons which have piled up on one of the plates in case (b).

(Take the permittivity of air = ε_0 = $8 \cdot 85 \times 10^{-12}$ F m^{-1}, electronic charge $e = 1 \cdot 60 \times 10^{-19}$ C.)

4. Explain what is meant by dielectric constant (relative permittivity). State *two* physical properties desirable in a material to be used as the dielectric in a capacitor.

A sheet of paper $4 \cdot 0$ cm wide and $1 \cdot 5 \times 10^{-3}$ cm thick between metal foil of the same width is used to make a $2 \cdot 0$ μF capacitor. If the dielectric constant (relative permittivity) of the paper is $2 \cdot 5$, what length of paper is required? (The electric space constant = $8 \cdot 85 \times 10^{-12}$ F m^{-1}.)   (J.M.B.)

5. What is meant by 'the polarisation of a molecule in an external electric field'?

Distinguish between polar and non-polar molecules.

Explain in terms of atomic structure how a dielectric increases the capacitance of a capacitor.

6. Derive an expression for the energy stored in a charged capacitor.

Explain how the energy stored in a parallel-plate capacitor changes when the distance between the plates is increased, the capacitor having first been connected (a) permanently, (b) momentarily, to a suitable d.c. voltage supply.

7. Derive an expression for the energy of a charged insulated conductor. Show that when such a conductor is connected to another insulated conductor at a lower potential there is always a loss of energy. What becomes of this energy?

A conductor A of capacitance C_1 is given a charge Q and then touched on an insulated conductor B of capacitance C_2. What fraction of the charge is transferred to B? A is then recharged to the same total charge as at first and again touched on B. If this process is repeated indefinitely what will B's final charge be?   (S.)

8. A parallel plate capacitor has plates of area A with a separation of a. Obtain an expression for its capacitance. If the capacitor is immersed in an oil of dielectric constant ε_r, what is now the value of

the capacitance? Can you give any physical explanation for the change in the value of the capacitance?

If the air capacitor is given an initial charge Q and is then immersed in the oil, what will be the change in the energy of the condenser? If instead of keeping Q constant, the potential difference between the plates is maintained, by connecting to a battery, what would then be the change in energy when the system is immersed in the oil? How do you account for these changes in energy?

(W. Special)

9. A capacitor consists of two parallel plates of area A mounted a distance x apart in a liquid of dielectric constant (relative permittivity) ε. The capacitor carries a charge Q. Calculate from first principles, proving any formulae you use:

(a) the energy W stored in the capacitor;

(b) the change of W if the separation between the plates is increased by a small amount δx;

(c) hence, or otherwise, the force F per unit area on each plate of the capacitor as a function of E, the electric field between the plates;

(d) the work M done against electrical forces in removing all the liquid from the space between the plates. (C. Special)

10. Define capacitance. Derive the expression for the effective capacitance of two capacitors of capacitances C_1 and C_2 arranged (a) in series, (b) in parallel.

Two capacitors of 9 μF and 6 μF capacitance are charged from d.c. sources to 100 V and 50 V respectively. The capacitors are then isolated from their charging sources and connected together:

(a) with the like plates connected, i.e. positive to positive and negative to negative,

(b) with the positive plate of each connected to the negative of the other.

Compare the energies of the system in the two cases and account for the difference. (A.E.B.)

11. Explain the meaning of the term capacitance as used in electrostatics.

A potential difference of 90 V is applied across uncharged capacitors of 2 μF, 3 μF and 1·5 μF connected in series. Across which capacitor is the potential difference least? Explain this and find the numerical value of this potential difference. (J.M.B.)

12. Discuss briefly the basis of the system of electrical units with which you are familiar.

An uncharged metal sphere, A, 15·0 cm in diameter, is connected by a long fine wire to a fixed metal sphere, diameter 0·50 cm touching which is an equal small metal sphere of mass 0·040 g, suspended by a vertical silk thread 100 cm long. When the spheres are charged the distance between the centres of the small spheres becomes 8·00 cm. A is isolated and then discharged to earth through a ballistic galvanometer of long period and low resistance, giving a throw of 200 divisions.

In a second experiment, a current is passed through a circular coil of two turns of radius 15·0 cm, set up with its plane vertical and in the magnetic meridian, in series with two resistors in parallel, whose resistances are in the proportion $1 : 10^7$. A small freely suspended needle at the centre of the coil is deflected through 38·7°. When by means of suitable switches the current in the larger resistor is allowed to flow for 1·00 s through the same ballistic galvanometer, a throw of 250 divisions occurs. Making any valid approximations, find a value for the permittivity of air. Comment on the result. (Assume the horizontal component of the earth's magnetic field to be $1·85 \times 10^{-5}$ tesla.) (L. Special adapted)

Answers to Questions

Chapter 1 (page 24)

5 (a) 3 C; (b) 1.88×10^{19} electrons
6 6.25×10^{-5} m s^{-1}; 8.84×10^{-5} m s^{-1}; 2.81×10^{-7} m
7 3.98×10^{-6} m; fractional increase $= \dfrac{2\epsilon}{l}$
9 3.6×10^6 J; (i) 2.5×10^2 V; (ii) 1.44×10^4 C

Chapter 2 (page 55)

4 1.25×10^{-1} N m^{-1}; 6.25×10^{-2} N m^{-1}
5 (a) 1.6×10^{-13} N; (b) 1.6×10^{-13} N
6 5.0×10^{-5} T
7 3.16×10^{-3} m
8 2.5×10^{-3} N m
9 2.12 A m^2
10 10.1 divisions per μA
12 4.78×10^{-1} A
13 4.5 A
14 Force $= \mu_0 I^2 = \mu_0 \times 10^2$ N; no couple
15 2.75×10^{-1} m and 9×10^{-3} m from mid-position
16 2 N
17 (a) 2.51×10^{-3} T; (b) 1.26×10^{-3} T; 0.8×10^{-5} T
18 8.55×10^{-3} A
19 $2.27 \times 10^{-1} \cos \alpha$ m
20 1.0 A; 4.1×10^{-5} T

Chapter 3 (page 84)

1 7.56×10^{-5} V
2 2×10^{-5} T; 4×10^{-5} T; angle of dip $= 63°\ 26'$
3 2×10^{-5} T 1.6×10^{-5} A
4 $\frac{1}{2} B\theta \sqrt{(gl^3)}$; $\theta = \sin^{-1}\left(\dfrac{BIl}{2mg}\right)$
5 2×10^{-5} C
7 5.92×10^{-1} T
8 2.96×10^{-5} Ω

9 5×10^{-3} T
11 32·3 divisions
12 1·43 T
16 (a) $7 \cdot 86 \times 10^{-5}$ V;   (b) $3 \cdot 09 \times 10^{-8}$ J
17 $7 \cdot 55 \times 10^{-1}$ V
20 $2 \cdot 1 \times 10^{-2}$ V

Chapter 4 (page 109)

6 $6 \cdot 28 \times 10^{-4}$ H m^{-1}
9 (a) 8×10^{-4} T; (b) 4×10^{-1} T; (c) $3 \cdot 992 \times 10^{-1}$ T

Chapter 5 (page 133)

4 $2 \cdot 1 \times 10^{-9}$ C
5 $-5 \cdot 97 \times 10^{-9}$ C; $-2 \cdot 99 \times 10^{-9}$ C
7 (a) $9 \cdot 0 \times 10^{5}$ N C^{-1} (or V m^{-1});   (b) $1 \cdot 44 \times 10^{-13}$ N
8 $5 \cdot 69 \times 10^{3}$ N C^{-1} (or V m^{-1}); $-7 \cdot 64 \times 10^{2}$ V
10 $1 \cdot 5 \times 10^{6}$ V
12 (a) $9 \cdot 0 \times 10^{4}$ N C^{-1} (or V m^{-1});   (b) $9 \cdot 0 \times 10^{3}$ V
14 (a) $8 \cdot 85 \times 10^{-10}$ C m^{-2};   (b) $2 \cdot 0 \times 10^{-4}$ m
15 $2 \cdot 5 \times 10^{10}$ electrons

Chapter 6 (page 152)

1 $7 \cdot 11 \times 10^{-4}$ F
3 (a) $1 \cdot 78 \times 10^{-8}$ C; (b) $8 \cdot 90 \times 10^{-8}$ C; (c) $5 \cdot 56 \times 10^{11}$ electrons
4 33·9 m
7 $\dfrac{C_2}{C_1 + C_2}$; $\dfrac{C_2}{C_1} \times Q$

8 Energy decrease $= \frac{1}{2} \dfrac{Q^2 a}{\epsilon_0 A} \left(1 - \dfrac{1}{\epsilon_r} \right)$;   energy increase $= \frac{1}{2} \dfrac{Q^2 a}{\epsilon_0 A} (\epsilon_r - 1)$

9 (a) $\frac{1}{2} \dfrac{Q^2 x}{\epsilon_0 \epsilon A}$;   (b) $\frac{1}{2} \dfrac{Q^2 \delta x}{\epsilon_0 \epsilon A}$;   (c) $\frac{1}{2} \epsilon_0 \epsilon E^2$;   (d) $\frac{1}{2} \dfrac{Q^2 x}{\epsilon_0 A} \left(1 - \dfrac{1}{\epsilon} \right)$

10 (a) $4 \cdot 8 \times 10^{-2}$ J;   (b) $1 \cdot 2 \times 10^{-2}$ J
11 20 V
12 $8 \cdot 8 \times 10^{-12}$ F m^{-1}

Index